Developing Mathematical Ideas

Number and Operations, Part 1

Building a System of Tens

Facilitator's Guide

A collaborative project by the staff and
participants of Teaching to the Big Ideas

Principal Investigators

Deborah Schifter
Virginia Bastable
Susan Jo Russell

with
Jill Bodner Lester
Linda Ruiz Davenport
Lisa Yaffee
Sophia Cohen

Dale Seymour Publications®
Parsippany, New Jersey

 **National Science Foundation**

This work was supported by the National Science Foundation under Grant Nos. ESI-9254393 and ESI-9050210. Any opinions, findings, conclusions, or recommendations expressed here are those of the authors and do not necessarily reflect the views of the National Science Foundation.

Additional support was provided by the Massachusetts Higher Education Coordinating Council and the Dwight D. Eisenhower Mathematics and Science Education Program.

Published by Dale Seymour Publications®, 299 Jefferson Road, Parsippany, NJ 07054.

Dale Seymour Publications® is an imprint of Addison Wesley Longman, Inc.

EXECUTIVE EDITOR: Catherine Anderson
PROJECT EDITOR: Beverly Cory
PRODUCTION/MANUFACTURING DIRECTOR: Janet Yearian
SENIOR PRODUCTION/MANUFACTURING COORDINATOR: Fiona Santoianni
DESIGN DIRECTOR: Phyllis Aycock
DESIGN MANAGER: Jeff Kelly
TEXT AND COVER DESIGN: Paula Shuhert
COMPOSITION: Joe Conte

ISBN 0-7690-0170-X
DS21962

1 2 3 4 5 6 7 8 9 10-ML-03 02 01 00 99

This product is printed on recycled paper

Teaching to the Big Ideas

Developing Mathematical Ideas (DMI) was developed as a collaborative project by the staff and participants of Teaching to the Big Ideas, an NSF Teacher Enhancement Project.

PROJECT DIRECTORS Deborah Schifter (EDC), Virginia Bastable (SummerMath for Teachers), Susan Jo Russell (TERC)

STAFF Sophia Cohen (EDC), Jill Bodner Lester (SummerMath for Teachers), Lisa Yaffee (TERC), Linda Ruiz Davenport (EDC)

PARTICIPANTS Allan Arnaboldi, Lisa Bailly, Audrey Barzey, Julie Berke, Nancy Buell, Yvonne Carpio, Rose Christiansen, Ann Connally, Nancy Dostal, Marcia Estelle, Becky Eston, Trish Farrington, Victoria Fink, Gail Gilmore, Nancy Horowitz, Debbie Jacques, Marcy Kitchener, Rick Last, Eileen Madison, Joyce McLaurin, Rena Moore, Amy Morse, Deborah O'Brien, Marti Ochs, Anne Marie O'Reilly, Hilory Paster, Jessica Redman, Priscilla Rhodes, Margie Riddle, Jan Rook, Doug Ruopp, Sherry Sajdak, Cynthia Schwartz, Karen Schweitzer, Lisa Seyferth, Susan Bush Smith, Diane Stafford, Liz Sweeney, Nora Toney, Polly Wagner, Carol Walker, and Steve Walkowicz, representing the public schools of Amherst, Belchertown, Boston, Brookline, Lincoln, Newton, Northampton, Pelham, South Hadley, Southampton, Springfield, Westfield, and Williamsburg, Massachusetts, and the Atrium School in Watertown, Massachusetts

VIDEO DEVELOPMENT Susan Jo Russell, Judy Storeygard, David Smith, and Megan Murray (TERC), Jill Bodner Lester (SummerMath for Teachers)

CONSULTANTS, *BUILDING A SYSTEM OF TENS* Deborah Ball and Magdalene Lampert (University of Michigan), Kathryn Irwin (University of Auckland), Terry Wood (Purdue University)

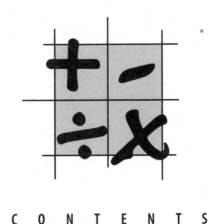

C O N T E N T S

Orientation to the Materials   1

Tips for Facilitators   4

Detailed Agendas   17

How to Use the Agendas   18

Preparation for the Seminar   23

Session 1   Children's Algorithms for Adding and Subtracting Two-Digit Numbers   27

Session 2   Recognizing and Keeping Track of Groups of 10 While Operating   43

Session 3   Written Numerals and the Structure of Tens and Ones   53

Session 4   More on Addition and Subtraction of Two-Digit Numbers   63

Session 5   Multiplication of Multidigit Numbers   73

Session 6   Division with Multidigit Numbers   83

Session 7   Decimal Numbers   93

Session 8   Highlights of Related Research   101

Maxine's Journal   107

Introductory Note   108

September 10, Goals for the Seminar   109

September 11, Session 1   112

September 25, Session 2   119

October 9, Session 3   129

October 23, Session 4   136

November 6, Session 5   142

November 20, Session 6   151

December 4, Session 7   158

December 18, Session 8   164

Two Portraits of Change   171

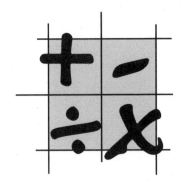

Orientation to the Materials

Developing Mathematical Ideas (DMI) is a series of professional development seminars designed to help teachers think through the major ideas of K–6 mathematics and examine how children develop those ideas. At the heart of the DMI materials are casebooks filled with classroom episodes, or cases, that illustrate the mathematical thinking of students as described by their teachers. In addition to reading and discussing these cases, participants in a DMI seminar view and discuss videotapes of mathematics classrooms; explore mathematics in lessons led by facilitators; share and discuss the work of their own students; plan, conduct, and analyze mathematics interviews of their students; write their own "cases"; analyze lessons from innovative elementary mathematics curricula; and read overviews of related research.

The major goals of the DMI seminars are to help participants

- learn more mathematics content themselves

- recognize key mathematical ideas with which their students are grappling

- appreciate the power and complexity of student thinking

- ask questions of students that will help them deepen their mathematical understanding

- analyze a particular activity to uncover the mathematics students will learn from it

- define and select mathematical objectives for their students

- make more mathematical connections for themselves, enhancing their ability to help their students do so

- learn how to *continue* learning about children and mathematics

Number and Operations is the focus of two DMI seminars: Part 1, *Building a System of Tens,* and Part 2, *Making Meaning for Operations.* In preparation are materials for three additional DMI seminars: two on

Geometry and one on Data Analysis.

The first seminar, *Building a System of Tens,* explores children's thinking to discover what they understand (and misunderstand) about place value in our base ten number system, and how their understanding affects their work with computation. As participants investigate children's thinking, they also explore the mathematics for themselves. Throughout this first seminar, they practice mental arithmetic, at first by sharing their strategies for adding and subtracting multidigit numbers. Many who come to the seminar believe that the algorithms they teach offer the only valid methods of computation, and those who invent their own strategies often feel a little ashamed, as though they are relying on a crutch or using less-sophisticated methods. Gradually teachers loosen the hold of these beliefs.

As participants begin to maneuver more fluently about our number system, they also begin thinking about properties of the operations. In particular, they develop models for multiplication and division, and consider how the distributive property is implicated in multiplying or dividing multidigit numbers. Finally they consider representations of decimal fractions and examine how ideas of place value, which they have been studying since the beginning of the seminar, play out to the right of the decimal point. At every step, teachers of any level from kindergarten through sixth grade find something applicable to their own teaching experience.

The second seminar in the series, *Making Meaning for Operations,* examines the ways children come to make sense of addition, subtraction, multiplication, and division. The focus is on the variety of situations modeled by these operations. Later sessions of the seminar revisit the operations as they apply to fractions. Again, while teachers learn how children confront these mathematical issues, they are also exploring the mathematics for themselves. After all, today's teachers are themselves products of an educational system that has long emphasized rote memorization of math facts and rules for calculation. They, too, need to think through the variety of situations modeled by addition and subtraction; and they, too, need to examine various representations of multiplication and division. The work on operations with fractions is especially challenging for teachers. As is true for the first seminar, teachers of every level from kindergarten through sixth grade will find pertinent ideas in the cases and the activities.

The two seminars on Number and Operations were designed for use as a stand-alone course, typically presented over a full school year to practicing teachers who meet at regularly scheduled intervals, usually weekly or biweekly. Each seminar is designed for 8 three-hour sessions, or a total of 16 sessions (48 hours) for the two seminars. However, the seminars have been presented successfully in a variety of formats (summer institutes, college courses) and with a variety of constituencies (undergraduate students, school administrators, parents). Notes from course facilitators of the pilot seminars, describing the ways in which they adapted the materials for some of these variations, are found in "Tips for Facilitators."

While the two Number and Operations seminars were originally designed to work in tandem, they may be presented singly in some circumstances. However, it is strongly advised that seminar participants attend Part 1, *Building a System of Tens,* before taking Part 2, *Making Meaning for Operations.* The ideas in Part 1 are more accessible to practicing and preservice teachers than are those in Part 2, and those who have had a chance to reflect on the material in Part 1 will be better prepared for the second seminar.

Materials for the DMI seminars

Each Number and Operations seminar requires three types of materials: a casebook for each individual participant, a videotape to be shown during the seminar, and a facilitator's guide, with detailed agendas and background reading on the issues of facilitating teacher change.

Casebook Participants read a separate casebook for each seminar. The casebooks each contain 25–30 cases that were written by K–6 teachers representing schools in urban, suburban, and rural settings. The cases are grouped into chapters based on a particular mathematical theme. An introduction to each chapter orients the reader to the major theme of that set of cases. Each casebook concludes with an essay titled "Highlights of Related Research." Having previously explored children's mathematical thinking through the eyes of classroom teachers in the cases, seminar participants now consider the same issues from a research perspective.

Videotape Each Number and Operations seminar includes a videocassette, with separate segments to be viewed and discussed in particular seminar sessions. The videos show students solving problems and dealing with the same ideas participants are encountering in the casebooks. The videos were filmed in a variety of classroom settings, with children and teachers of different races and ethnic groups and a balance of girls and boys. While the print cases allow readers to examine student thinking at their own pace and return as needed to ponder and analyze particular passages, the video cases offer viewers the opportunity to listen to real student voices in real time. They also provide vivid images of classrooms organized around student thinking.

Facilitator's guide A facilitator's guide for each seminar helps presenters plan the eight sessions, understand the major ideas to be explored in each session, identify strategies useful in leading case discussions and mathematics activities, and think through the issues of teacher change. In "Tips for Facilitators," users read advice on implementation issues from those who have field-tested the materials—for example, what to listen for when participants work in small groups, and how to ease the difficulties of whole-group discussions. The "Detailed Agendas" include lists to help the facilitator prepare for each session (what to read, materials to collect, handouts to duplicate), followed by an outline detailing the recommended sequence and timing of activities.

Two documents at the end of the guide offer informative glimpses of what happens in a DMI seminar. "Maxine's Journal," written as the reflective journal of a (fictional) facilitator, describes an amalgam of very real people and events encountered during DMI pilot seminars. This session-by-session journal helps facilitators think about the mathematical and pedagogical issues to be addressed in each session, as well as the larger theme of teacher change. "Two Portraits of Change," with examples drawn from actual participants' written work, tracks the learning of two particular teachers through the course of the seminar, illustrating the changes they go through.

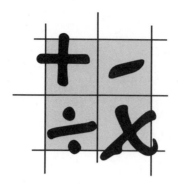

Tips for Facilitators

The DMI seminars were piloted in a range of settings by facilitators with varying professional backgrounds. These facilitators included university faculty, staff development personnel, and teachers working with colleagues. For some, leading a DMI seminar was their first experience as a teacher-leader or teacher educator; others had many years of service in this role.

Through conversations and written reflections, the seminar facilitators provided valuable feedback about their experiences piloting these materials. The following tips include their suggestions, some directly quoted, for getting oriented to the materials, preparing for individual seminar sessions, creating a community of inquiry, facilitating discussion, understanding participants' emotions, responding to the written portfolio assignments, and adjusting the course to different formats and constituencies. This section concludes with an anno-tated bibliography of recommended supplemental readings.

Getting oriented

Before conducting a DMI seminar, familiarize yourself with both the overall goals of the course and the materials provided. You will be using these materials to support teachers as they (1) recognize themselves and the children they teach as mathematical thinkers, (2) deepen their understanding of the core ideas in the elementary mathematics curriculum, (3) explore how children develop those ideas, (4) reflect on their own experiences to analyze the process of learn-ing, and (5) rethink their teaching practice.

As the course facilitator, you will lead your group in the following types of activities.

■ **Case discussions** In these discussions of the casebook, teachers strive to follow student thinking, work on mathematical ideas for themselves, reflect on their own learning, and consider the types of classroom settings and teaching strategies that support the development of student understanding.

- **Viewing the videotapes** On the videotapes, teachers see episodes that capture both classroom atmosphere and student affect. These tapes give participants invaluable glimpses of students' mathematical thinking in process.

- **Math activities** Through activities similar to those faced by students in the print and video cases, the teachers develop, share, analyze, and refine their own mathematical thinking.

- **Exploring innovative curricular materials** By studying selected materials from existing mathematics curricula, teachers work to connect their seminar learnings with the mathematical tasks they set for their students.

- **Discussing related research** This concluding activity in each seminar creates an integrated picture of the mathematical themes under consideration, connecting the events observed in the cases and in participants' own classrooms to the work of the research community.

In addition, teachers participating in a DMI seminar complete regular written "portfolio assignments" between sessions; these are sometimes reflections on what they are learning in the seminar, and at other times, a closer look into their own students' mathematical thinking.

To become familiar with the flow of mathematical ideas in the seminar materials, we suggest that a facilitator read the introduction to the casebook, the overviews of the cases in each chapter, and the concluding essay on related research. We also recommend reading portions of "Maxine's Journal," a composite account (from a facilitator's perspective) of one prototypical group's seminar experience. In addition, you may find it useful to examine some of the cases, look through the detailed agendas and handouts, and read "Two Portraits of Change," case studies drawn from two teacher-participants' actual portfolio writings.

Preparing for a session

Once you are familiar with the goals and components of the DMI materials, the next step is to prepare for individual sessions. For each session, you should read the cases first, then the relevant entry of "Maxine's Journal," and, where applicable, do the math activity, view the related video clips, or familiarize yourself with selected lessons from innovative curricula. As you do this work, think through the issues raised by the set of activities for that session. What ideas about mathematics, learning, and teaching should emerge as teachers participate in the investigations and discussions? How are these ideas illustrated in the cases? How might they arise in the other activities? What questions might you pose to call attention to these ideas? As one facilitator wrote:

> *I realize now more than ever how important it is to be really prepared and to have thought through the issues, mathematical and otherwise, that might arise. Having a sense of what the important points are that you want people to be exploring, and the direction in which you want them to be headed, is crucial. However, it is also important to realize that sometimes "the way there" might turn out to be different from the route you anticipated.*

Besides planning for issues likely to arise during discussions, you must think through the order of the activities and set a timetable. Organize the materials so everything is ready for each session; having the readings, handouts, videotapes, video equipment, and manipulatives at hand before a session begins saves time and allows you to concentrate on seminar participants. Suggestions for time allotments and the order of activities are given in the session agendas, along with detailed lists of the materials you will need.

Creating a community of inquiry

One objective of the DMI seminars is to establish a "community of inquiry," a sense of shared purpose and norms of conduct that allow participants to focus on ideas, both their own and those of their colleagues. This is not accomplished in a single session, but develops slowly. As one facilitator wrote, "I believe this climate of inquiry is created through careful work and planning over time with caring facilitators and willing participants. It never just happens. It requires constant nurturing, sensitivity, and organization."

Each teacher brings to the seminar his or her own experiences and ideas from which the others—and you, too—can learn much. It is your job, as facilitator, to encourage every participant to put those experiences and ideas on the table.

The tone of the seminar should be set at the very first meeting by establishing that all ideas are valued and that questioning is perceived as a sign of strength, not weakness. Listening to what is said, rather than for what one expects, is crucial to creating a community in which all ideas are heard and respected. What is the participant saying? What are the ideas behind the words? How are his or her ideas related to those of the

other participants? How are they different? "The purpose of [our] work is not about getting other teachers to think the same way, but rather to encourage an environment in which participants value, reflect on, and question their own ideas and the perspectives of others."

Another facilitator wrote, "As facilitators, we must create a pathway for learning that is challenging but safe. We must listen carefully to the comments our new fellow-travelers will share, empathize with their frustrations, help them through times of vulnerability, and share in the pleasures of their new insights."

Communicating clarity of purpose at the start of the seminar is vital to setting the tone. For instance, by making it clear that sessions will begin and end on time, you convey a message of commitment. "Careful, productive, and appropriate use of time is a courtesy to the participants which indicates that you are respectful of their decisions to be there in the midst of their busy lives and tight schedules."

Other ground rules to be addressed at the first meeting relate to assignments and attendance. Unlike many college courses or staff workshops, the success of the DMI seminar depends on participant preparation. Written homework and thoughtful reaction to assigned readings provide a starting point for the work of the session. Participants may have other expectations, so this should be stated explicitly. Attending each meeting with completed assignments prepares teachers to participate in planned activities and discussions and is a sign of respect for other members of the group.

Not all participants will feel comfortable speaking up or offering their opinions in whole-group discussion. Their involvement with the ideas of the DMI seminar can take many forms. People may be listening care fully, following the discussion, reflecting on what they hear, and formulating opinions of their own without sharing their thoughts aloud. Over time, participants will need support in seeking their own levels of verbal engagement. Among the strategies that encourage participation are allowing enough "wait time" for people to formulate their ideas, asking for a paraphrase of an idea, or asking for agreement or disagreement on particular points. During whole-group discussion, facilitators should ask clarifying questions, call attention to connections between participants' ideas, and pose questions designed to move the discussion forward.

The second session of Number and Operations, Part 1: *Building a System of Tens* includes an activity designed to help participants set group norms for respectful interaction. These norms should be revisited periodically as the seminars continue. Participants need to feel safe, whether sharing hypotheses or feelings. Adults' beliefs have developed over many years, and transforming those beliefs is a complicated process. An environment of inquiry, in which everyone's thinking is taken seriously and challenging someone's ideas is viewed as a sign of respect, must be cultivated.

Facilitating group discussion

For seminar participants, small-group discussion provides a more intimate, certainly less intimidating forum for sharing their perspectives than does discussion among the whole group. In the small group, participants can explore mathematical ideas for themselves and pose questions about teaching, about learning, and about student understanding—all of which may feel risky in the larger group. Furthermore, in a group of 2 to 4 people, there is more time to air ideas than in a group of 15 to 30.

While participants are meeting in small groups, what is the facilitator's role? When should you begin to move among the groups? When should you ask a question, add a comment, or just be a silent observer?

After setting small groups to work, allow time for them to get into meaningful discussion without being distracted by the facilitator. Then, once such discussion is underway, listen in on each of the small groups to get an overview of participants' interests, questions, and concerns. Moving among and stopping by each of the groups also communicates interest in the ideas being discussed and reassures participants that their discussions are useful and productive.

Sometimes, people in small groups are "off task." It may then be necessary for the facilitator to focus the discussion on a specific point: evidence of mathematics learning presented in the cases, say, or a question the group might address through the math activity. If someone in the group is particularly engaged by the seminar task, questions inviting the rest of the group to consider her or his ideas are helpful: "What do you think about what [participant's name] is saying?"

Small-group discussion offers opportunities for the facilitator to monitor group dynamics. How are group members relating to one another? Are all the participants contributing to the discussion? Are participants' ideas being respected?

[Interacting with small groups] is not about having a right thing to do, but having a stock of alternatives and knowing when to call on which. Ask questions when the group needs to move, ask questions to understand their thinking, listen to affirm, refer to what you heard to encourage someone to speak, or refer to it because you think they can make a connection that might be useful.

Listening to the small-group discussions helps you gather information and make decisions about the whole-group discussion to follow.

To initiate whole-group discussion, you might choose among several strategies:

- Bring out an issue that caused confusion in small groups: "It seems that lots of people are struggling with the idea that . . . and so I thought we could come together to see if we can sort it out."

- Begin with an idea that some groups found stimulating: "Many of you were discussing [issue X]. Now I think it would be worth our while to discuss where you agree and where your interpretations and perspectives differ."

- Highlight a point made in one small group that is important for everyone to consider: "[Participant's name] said something that left me thinking . . . ."

- Draw the group's attention to an issue that had been ignored in small groups: "As I went from group to group, I heard lots of interesting and important ideas, but I didn't hear anyone talking about [issue Y]."

The strategy you employ to begin a whole-group discussion depends on the ideas you want to pursue and the issues that arise during small-group time. In general, however, whole-group discussion should not be a simple rehash of what went on in small groups. Its purpose should be to raise discussion to a new level, "to encourage ideas, thoughts, and conjectures to surface for all to grapple with."

There are a few strategies particular to facilitating *case* discussions: The whole group can begin with one of the focus questions on the handout you distributed for that session. As the discussion of children's mathematics unfolds, you should ask that particular line numbers in the casebook be cited. This technique draws everyone into the specifics of the case, focuses the conversation on the mathematical ideas of the children, and helps avoid generalized critiques of classrooms and teaching strategies. If necessary, you can slow the pace of discussion and provide time for thinking about and reacting to what is being said by recording, on easel paper or the board, ideas that emerge from the group.

Understanding participants' emotions

People enter the seminar with expectations based on their past staff-development experiences, experiences that may differ from those DMI offers. For example, some participants may feel disappointed that they are not leaving each session with activities for their classrooms. On the other hand, they may feel excited about learning the mathematics for themselves, investigating children's mathematical thinking, or following the development of children's mathematical understanding over time. One participant wrote about how she had to readjust her thinking to appreciate what she was learning:

I compare it to approaching a glass and thinking that you are going to be drinking chocolate milk and ending up drinking tomato juice. At first you are surprised and then you change your mental image and readjust your taste buds.

She explained that once she understood what the seminar would be, she began to enjoy it. ("I do like tomato juice!") She went on to say that she appreciates seeing things in new ways and discovering a better practice for her students.

You may have to tell participants explicitly that the seminar may challenge their present ways of thinking and even their conceptions about what it means to be a good teacher. Feelings of ambivalence or resistance are to be expected.

Early in one of the pilot seminars, a participant wrote about how the course had shaken her confidence, even as it promised a new and enhanced professional identity:

After the first two sessions I asked myself, where were we going? I didn't know. It was then that I started to pay attention to the word "inquiry." I thought I was already doing this. I'd begun to have self-doubts and a feeling of frustration was beginning to build. . . .

My first deduction after three sessions was, hmm—I really wasn't paying enough attention to my students' thinking. I was still doing a lot of assuming.

So you are making me think and you're shaking me out of complacency. What do I expect?—to get better at what I do. I think you're taking me down a completely new road.

Although listening carefully to what participants are saying about the seminar is often unsettling, you as facilitator do need to be aware of their questions and frustrations. Attending to participants in this way communicates your concern and respect for them. At times, you may find that small adaptations alleviate their problems. At other times, you may learn that their frustrations are part of the process of learning and do not indicate a problem at all. For example, after reviewing participants' evaluations at the end of her seminar, one facilitator wrote that when respondents gave their overall seminar experience the highest rating, "very valuable," she was pleasantly surprised, "since participants expressed significant frustration, critical questioning, anger, discomfort, and resistance throughout the course."

Because it is not possible or appropriate for all participants to express concerns, questions, and frustrations during seminar discussions, it is useful to have a variety of strategies for keeping in touch with individuals. "Exit cards" are an efficient way of gathering this information. By posing one to three questions for participants to respond to briefly, in writing, before they leave each session, you may discover what people are learning, what they are concerned about, and what questions they have. Specific suggestions for exit-card questions appear in a later section of this guide.

Responding to portfolio assignments

Throughout a DMI seminar, participants complete writing assignments that they collect in portfolios. Some assignments encourage teachers to examine the mathematical thinking of their own students; other writings provide a vehicle for participants to articulate and clarify their ideas. Still others help participants reflect on how those ideas are developing over time. For example, participants collect and analyze samples of student work before and after each seminar. By looking over these assignments, participants are able to see how their expectations for their students have changed.

The facilitator's response to portfolio assignments is important because it validates the participants' work and indicates your interest in their opinions and ideas. For some assignments, you might acknowledge each individual's ideas through comments you make at the next session. You can also use your summary of people's ideas to move the group into a discussion on these points. Sometimes you might excerpt quotes from participants' writings and organize them on a handout that teachers can take away to reread and ponder; this provides a way to share ideas while high-lighting the issues you consider important. In other instances, you might choose to respond to each individual in writing.

Participants should receive feedback about every assignment, sometimes from other seminar members and sometimes from you, the facilitator. Decisions about how to respond will be based on the type of assignment and the goal of that particular seminar session. When the assignment is a journal-type reflection, focused on each participant's learning experience, an individual written response works well. On the other hand, a written response to the group, with excerpts from individual work, allows participants to see the variety of issues addressed in the writings taken together. Finally, some portfolio assignments are explicitly intended to provide a starting point for class discussion. In these cases, the *participants* offer feedback to one another, and a response from the facilitator may be unnecessary.

Adapting to different formats

The DMI seminars were originally planned for weekly or biweekly sessions of three hours each, with eight of these sessions in each seminar. However, the materials have been adapted to a variety of formats. Following are comments from facilitators on some of the formats they have used for the two Number and Operations seminars.

Seminar meeting for three hours weekly

"I really like this format. It's very intense, yet enough time between sessions that participants have time to reflect, try things in classrooms, etc. Even when we had two weeks between sessions (because of vaca-

tion), participants still admitted to doing the work the night before!"

Seminar meeting for three hours after school, biweekly

"Meeting every other week gave both the participants and the facilitators some time to reflect on the work we were doing. As a facilitator who was at the same time a classroom teacher, it was important for me to have the week between to prepare with my co-facilitators and to reflect on our participants' work. The participants commented that meeting every other week made it seem more manageable, in terms of the amount of time they spent in class. They also liked having time between sessions to try things they had been thinking about."

Seminar meeting for three hours on Saturdays, biweekly

"To my surprise, the teachers don't complain about spending their Saturday mornings this way. In contrast to after-school seminars, they arrive rested and refreshed. We'll meet approximately every other week throughout the year to cover both Part 1 and Part 2."

Seminar meeting for 90 minutes weekly

"We chose this format to accommodate child-care issues for the teachers in our school. Having weekly meetings for an entire year seems to maintain a high level of 'mindfulness' about math, individual commitment, and openness to the work; it also offers an invaluable cohesiveness to the group and to our shared purpose. The drawback is that the case discussions and the math activities that support examination of the cases do not take place in the same session."

Seminar meeting for 90 minutes biweekly

"This format encourages participation by teachers who are involved in numerous after-school activities or who have young children at home. One disadvantage is that it spreads each session over a month; I'm now feeling the need to move more quickly. It's also not possible to do both Part 1 and Part 2 in one school year unless you add some sessions at other times."

Each seminar covered in four full-day workshops

"Teachers who participated in the four full-day meetings explained that, because of child-care issues and other concerns, they would have been unable to attend after-school meetings. They said they liked the feeling of shedding their teaching responsibilities in the morning, to have the experience of being the student all day. And they liked the intensity. Issues to think about include how to cover teachers' classrooms, how to rearrange the agendas, and what to do about the homework assignments, the interview of a student, case writing, and so forth."

Summer school course, three and a half hours, twice a week

"I taught a summer school course that met twice a week, for three and a half hours each session, over a four-week period (though it should have been longer). I didn't follow the DMI agendas exactly, but we worked through all of Parts 1 and 2. Students read two or three cases for each class and, as much as possible, I posed problems for the class to try before they were asked to read about what the children did. I also selected particular focus questions for students to read, think, and write about before the case discussions."

Summer institute, 10 full days

"We scheduled sessions so that two afternoons were spent conducting interviews. Teachers were told ahead of time which days they would be interviewing children and were asked to make an appointment with a child. They also had long lunch breaks with enough time to reread the cases we would be discussing in the afternoon. Although we had to sacrifice the assignments to bring in student work and write cases—teachers could not be testing out new ideas in their classrooms as the seminar progressed—the concentration and immersion into the work was a positive."

Semester course for undergraduates

"In keeping with the structure of our college schedule, DMI for undergraduates met for 28 sessions, each 75 minutes long, twice a week for 14 weeks. Working our way through both parts, students had a reading assignment and a portfolio assignment due each week."

Working with different constituencies

The DMI seminars address fundamental issues of mathematics education—understanding *what* students are to learn and *how* they learn it. Although the materials were initially written for use with practicing teachers, other constituencies concerned about the same issues—including undergraduates, school administrators, and parents—have benefited from DMI seminars as well. Facilitators of these seminars describe the approaches they took.

DMI as an undergraduate course

"We followed the DMI curriculum closely, modifying the timing of the agendas to fit the college schedule. Weekly requirements included a reading assignment from the casebook and a portfolio entry. Each student was paired with a local teacher who has been particularly reflective about his or her own practice, to provide access to classrooms for the portfolio assignments. The only modification made to the portfolio assignments was to eliminate those requiring the collection and analysis of student work."

DMI as a seminar for parents

"My co-facilitator and I presented Part 1, *Building a System of Tens*, to parents. We met in the evening once a week for eight weeks in a row. Our aims for parents were to help them learn to listen to their children, to give them an opportunity to learn mathematics in the way that their children are learning it, and to help them develop a curiosity about the ways their children think, mathematically and otherwise. The parents read the cases for each session, just as teachers would. Writing assignments were only slightly modified so that the language was specific to parents. Instead of having parents bring in 'student work' in the first session, we asked parents to write a 'math autobiography' to share in small groups with other parents. This helped set the stage for us to reexamine our mathematics understanding in the group. Instead of responding in writing to each parent's homework assignment, we often gave 'homework updates' at the beginning of a class. The two facilitators, who took turns reading all of the homework writing between sessions, culled quotes to read aloud. In this way, the parents heard about each other's thinking

in their own voices. Otherwise the seminar ran just as it would for teachers."

For more information about using DMI with parents, see "Learning to Listen: Lessons from a Mathematics Seminar for Parents," by Amy Morse and Polly Wagner, in the February 1998 issue of *Teaching Children Mathematics, 4 (6)*, pp. 361–364.

Administrators participating in a DMI seminar for teachers

"It's been extremely interesting to have an administrator in our course for teachers. He decided to take the course because he felt he had asked his staff to undertake something very difficult in learning how to teach a new math curriculum which is so different from what teachers had always been expected to do. He was surprised to learn, through the seminar, that what he expects of his staff is much more difficult to achieve than he ever anticipated. Elementary math concepts are complex! Trying to understand what kids 'know' is even more complex. Figuring out how to teach on the basis of what kids understand is also difficult. Since he has been able to verbalize these things in front of his teachers, they feel that he understands and appreciates what they are going through as they struggle to create a deeper understanding of what mathematics is and how children make sense of it.

"So, one thing that our resident administrator brings to the course is the validation of his staff through a willingness to engage in the process he has asked them to become involved with. Another thing he brings is a systemic perspective on reform. It is clear that the math ideas which so intrigue the teachers are of much less concern to him. He is interested in how we can get parents, teacher training programs, district and state administrators, the public at large, standardized-test designers, textbook publishers, and the like to see math differently, and to realize that children's thinking must become the center of instruction if children are ever going to understand what they are doing. The fact that he raises these big issues provides further reassurance to teachers that their time and effort isn't being wasted every other week."

DMI as professional development for teacher educators, staff developers, and teacher-leaders

"Participants in this seminar engaged with the materials at many different levels. For some, the bulk of their attention was given to analyzing student thinking and working on their own mathematics. For others, participating in DMI activities provided an opportunity to reflect on goals for teachers' professional development and analyze how the different activities are designed to achieve those goals. In addition, 'Maxine's Journal' and 'Two Portraits of Change' were used as cases to inquire into issues of facilitation and teacher learning."

Visiting the DMI web site

The Education Development Center (EDC) maintains a web site with information about the DMI curriculum:

http://www.edc.org/LTT/CDT/DMIcur.html

Along with links related to other projects from EDC's Center for the Development of Teaching, you will find information on studies being done related to the use and impact of these professional development seminars. The link "Advice from DMI Users" leads to pages where facilitators who have used these materials share some of their reflections, strategies, and discoveries for presenting DMI in varying formats and for interacting with the participants.

For further study

Much of the videotaped material that is included in the DMI Number and Operations units is excerpted from another staff development program, *Relearning to Teach Arithmetic* (Dale Seymour Publications, 1999), which uses videotape filmed in classrooms as the primary tool for studying children's thinking about whole-number computation. After completing the DMI seminars, groups of teachers may want to consider the *Relearning to Teach Arithmetic* packages for further study.

Bibliography

Seminar participants may sometimes find it helpful to refer to supplemental readings that address particular concerns or interests related to issues raised by the DMI seminars. Following are suggested references.

Duckworth, E. (1987). *The having of wonderful ideas and other essays on teaching and learning.* New York: Teachers College Press.

Well-known educator and student of children's thinking Eleanor Duckworth has collected many of her essays in this volume. The essays consider a range of issues in teaching and learning in a variety of content areas, including mathematics, science, and language. Each essay provides an opportunity for educators to think more deeply about their practice as they consider the author's belief that "the having of wonderful ideas is the essence of intellectual development."

Hiebert, J., Carpenter, T., Fennema, E., Fuson, K., Wearne, D., Murray, H., Olivier, A., & Human, P. (1997). *Making sense: Teaching and learning mathematics with understanding.* Portsmouth, NH: Heinemann.

This book is based on the authors' work in four separate research programs, all of which investigated the effects of new instructional approaches in the teaching of mathematics. Out of their ongoing discussion, a consensus emerged about what features are essential to support students' mathematical understandings. By describing these features and offering pictures of several classrooms that exhibit them, the authors create a framework within which elementary teachers can reflect on their own practice and think about what it means to teach for understanding.

Kamii, C. (1989). *Young children continue to reinvent arithmetic, 2nd grade: Implications of Piaget's theory.* New York: Teachers College Press.

Children use what they already know and understand to solve mathematics problems. Kamii focuses on the sense-making of second-grade students as they invent their own computation strategies for addition and subtraction. Kamii has authored similar books for other grades.

Mokros, J., Russell, S. J., & Economopoulos, K. (1996). *Beyond facts and flash cards.* Portsmouth, NH: Heinemann.

This book is both a resource and a consumer's guide to mathematics learning for parents of elementary school children. Its aims are to build parents' understanding of, and demand for, solid mathematics education for their children and to encourage the incorporation of real mathematics into everyday family activities. The book gives extended examples of how parents can make changes: by learning what mathematics really is and solving mathematical problems for themselves; by tuning into the mathematics that interests their children; and by doing mathematics with their children the same way that they read, ride bikes, or make music with them—with a sense of adventure, surprise, challenge, and togetherness.

Mokros, J., Russell, S. J., & Economopoulos, K. (1995). *Beyond arithmetic: Changing mathematics in the elementary classroom.* Palo Alto, CA: Dale Seymour Publications.

Elementary teachers have many questions about current efforts to transform mathematics instruction: Why does the approach advocated by the reform movement give less attention to algorithms and procedures that have formed the backbone of traditional mathematics instruction? Will children really learn important mathematical ideas, and be prepared for their futures, if we radically change the nature of mathematics instruction? Is it worth the risk? This book helps teachers grapple with these issues and figure out how to begin to transform their teaching. Topics include the role of innovative curriculum materials, new modes of assessment, what a reform classroom looks like, talking with parents, and common questions teachers ask.

National Council of Teachers of Mathematics. (in press). *Principles and standards for school mathematics.* Reston, VA: Author.

This document lays out a set of principles and standards for the teaching and learning of mathematics that are intended to guide the improvement of mathematics education in coming years. As of early 1999, a discussion draft had been made public and the *Standards* authors were soliciting feedback for the final version, scheduled to be published in April 2000. *Principles and Standards for School Mathematics* builds on the foundation that was established by three earlier NCTM *Standards* documents: *Curriculum and Evaluation Standards for School Mathematics* (1989), *Professional Standards for Teaching Mathematics* (1991), and *Assessment Standards for School Mathematics* (1995).

Ohanian, S. (1992). *Garbage pizza, patchwork quilts, and math magic.* New York: W. H. Freeman.

The author, a teacher and freelance writer, traveled to schools across the country and documented the changes she saw happening in elementary mathematics classes. She recounts stories of teachers and students engaging in exciting mathematics and writes about such critical issues as the administrator-teacher partnership and communicating with parents.

Parker, R. (1993). *Mathematical power: Lessons from a classroom.* Portsmouth, NH: Heinemann.

In this complex, realistic picture of a fifth-grade class whose teacher tries to realize the goals set by the NCTM *Standards,* we see the teacher and her mentor select mathematics activities that will promote what they want their students to learn, establish a climate of inquiry in the classroom, and figure out what it means to teach and learn mathematics. A useful section on assessment and the use of portfolios is included.

Rowan, T., & Bourne, B. (1994). *Thinking like mathematicians: Putting the K–4 NCTM Standards into practice.* Portsmouth, NH: Heinemann.

In this book the authors consider, from a developmental perspective, children's construction of mathematical meaning. As they describe implementation of the NCTM *Standards* in grades K–4, they offer vignettes that highlight children's thinking and illustrate mathematics teaching and learning in several classrooms. The book ends with a chapter of questions and answers about implementing the NCTM *Standards* in the classroom.

Schifter, D., & Fosnot, C. T. (1993). *Reconstructing mathematics education: Stories of teachers meeting the challenge of reform.* New York: Teachers College Press.

Case studies of teachers show the struggles, doubts, and successes they experience as they work to change their mathematics instruction. Descriptions of classrooms include second graders hypothesizing about even and odd numbers, third graders demonstrating the commutativity of multiplication, and sixth graders puzzling over the mysteries of fractions. In each situation, the authors consider the teacher's intentions in designing the activity, the instructional decisions she makes as the children engage in it, and her reflections afterward. This book is particularly recommended for those who want to learn more about emotional aspects of teacher change.

Schifter, D. (Ed.). (1996). *What's happening in math class? Volume 1: Envisioning new practices through teacher narratives.* New York: Teachers College Press.

Schifter, D. (Ed.). (1996). *What's happening in math class? Volume 2: Reconstructing professional identities.* New York: Teachers College Press.

The two volumes of *What's Happening in Math Class?* contain 22 reflective, first-person narratives written by K–12 classroom teachers and nine essays by teacher educators. Volume 1 explores how basic pedagogical principles are put into play in day-to-day classroom life. It takes on such issues as establishing a community of inquiry in an elementary classroom and reaching *all* students. Volume 2 examines the experience of change and growth as teachers take on new roles in transforming their practice, including the history of a mathphobic sixth-grade teacher who confronts her fears and moves beyond.

Detailed Agendas

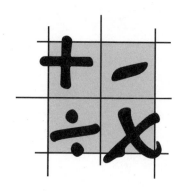

How to Use the Agendas

When I started co-facilitating a DMI seminar with a colleague, I felt glued to the facilitator's guide. I'd prepare for a session by reading the sections I was responsible for and trying to figure out how I was going to remember to say everything that was in the guide. In fact, I remember clutching the guide during a few early sessions as I facilitated discussions so that I wouldn't forget anything. Then I had the chance to meet with other people piloting the material and we talked about this. I was relieved to hear other people were having those feelings. The discussion turned to how do you make the material your own, really own it, yet keep the original intent of it intact. I thought about that for a long time. Instead of trying to memorize what the guide said, that became my focus when planning for a session. — a DMI facilitator

After the first few sessions of DMI, I was feeling a little uncomfortable. It seemed like I was marching through the agenda as outlined without seeing connections. There never seemed to be enough time to do the experiences, and we'd stop one to move on to another. That didn't feel right to me, but since it was my first time facilitating a seminar, I thought it was important to follow the guide. But then two amazing things happened. I realized that the same issues about place value were coming up repeatedly, and had been coming up all along. It didn't really matter if we were doing a math activity, discussing the cases, or watching the video, the conversation continued to be about important mathematical ideas and how the children were thinking about those ideas. I also realized that the agenda was a helpful guide, but because the conversations from one activity or session to the next revolved around the same ideas, it was OK not to feel closure for every experience. We could move on, accomplish our work, and I could feel confident that questions raised would be addressed in future sessions. — a DMI facilitator

The Developing Mathematical Ideas seminars support teachers as they explore the mathematics of the elementary curriculum for themselves and examine the way children develop mathematical ideas across the grades. Each seminar coordinates the discussion of print and video cases with a variety of other activities: mathematical explorations for adults, investigations of the mathematical thinking done by seminar participants' own students, analyses of activities from innovative curricula, and readings about related research.

The detailed agendas in this guide describe a sequence of activities for each DMI seminar session, with a suggested time allotment for each activity. A preparation and materials section for each session alerts facilitators to the supplies, handouts, and equipment needed for that session.

Included with the agendas are handouts ready to be duplicated for participants, including focus questions that guide the case discussions, mathematics activities to be done during the sessions, and the homework assignments that participants are to complete outside of the seminar sessions.

Format and timing

The facilitator's guides lay out a plan for covering both DMI seminars on Number and Operations in 16 sessions that meet for 3 hours each. However, facilitators have conducted DMI seminars in other configurations. For example, one facilitator used the DMI materials in an undergraduate setting with classes that met for 75 minutes, twice a week, over a 14-week semester. Another facilitator, working with in-service teachers, used 24 two-hour sessions. Still other programs used the DMI materials in summer workshops meeting on a daily basis. While the agendas spell out the order and a suggested duration for the activities in each session, you can adapt them to fit your situation.

Trying to follow the suggested time allotment for each activity—for example, a 40-minute case discussion, a 25-minute videotape, and a 15-minute math activity—may seem to fragment the session. However, the mathematical theme of the session provides coherence; ideas that emerge during one activity are revisited in another. In general, you should follow the suggested timing for the activities rather than expand one at the expense of another. For example, if participants want to continue a case discussion beyond the allotted time, it is likely that the mathematical issues that are engaging them in the cases will also be addressed through the next activity. In such a situation, you could acknowledge that you see the participants are doing some important thinking and assure them that turning to this new activity will allow them to continue their discussions. On the other hand, if the discussion of the cases feels finished before the allotted time, you might end that activity and make more time for the next.

Facilitators have reported how important it was for them to have a sense of the intention of each session and of the DMI seminar as a whole. Examining the issues raised in the introductions to each chapter of the casebook and reading "Maxine's Journal" can provide a starting point for this understanding. As you prepare for the session, consider what you want your group to get from each activity and how that learning contributes to the overall goal of the session. Once you know what you want to accomplish in each session, you will be able to use the agenda suggestions flexibly to suit your purposes.

These agendas assume that soon after the DMI seminar Part 1, *Building a System of Tens*, you will be presenting Part 2, *Making Meaning for Operations*. If you are planning to present only Part 1 of the seminar, you will need to reorganize the last two sessions so that participants review their portfolios and complete an evaluation form at the final meeting. For this purpose, you can modify the sample evaluation form provided in the facilitator's guide for *Making Meaning of Operations*.

Some facilitators may plan to offer the entire DMI seminar as two separate components, perhaps using *Building a System of Tens* during one school year and *Making Meaning for Operations* in the following year. In this case, note that the assignments suggested for the last session of Part 1 are preparation for the first session of Part 2. Therefore, you will need to either modify the agenda for the first session of Part 2 or distribute the appropriate assignment a week or so before that first meeting.

DMI seminar activities

Certain types of activities occur in every session; others may come up just once or twice in the entire seminar. Facilitators should be prepared to handle all of the following activities.

Reading and discussing the print cases

The casebook for *Building a System of Tens* is divided into chapters that correspond to the eight sessions of the DMI seminar. The introduction to each chapter describes that set of cases and highlights the general mathematical themes they address, giving the reader questions to consider while reading. Participants are expected to read both the introduction and the set of cases before the seminar meeting. Remind participants to consider the issues posed in the introduction as they read and discuss the cases. Since each case has something significant to offer, all cases should be read and consid-

ered. To guide the case discussion, distribute the appropriate set of focus questions (a handout) just before the discussion begins. These focus questions often refer to only a subset of the cases, drawing participants' attention to very specific issues. Once those have been addressed, it is often useful to revisit the more general questions posed in the introduction and then consider the entire set of cases.

Viewing and discussing the video cases

Six of the seminar sessions for *Building a System of Tens* include video cases of children working on mathematics problems. While the children in the videos are sharing approaches similar to those in the print cases, the videos bring the children to life in a way that is difficult to capture in print. The children mumble, fidget, write messily, and speak haltingly as they work to express their mathematical ideas. After seeing the video cases, participants often remark that they can then "hear" the students' voices when they read the print cases.

In some sessions, the video cases are viewed briefly and with little discussion. These clips serve mainly to provide images of classrooms in which students develop and share their approaches to mathematics problems. In other sessions, the video cases are the basis for seminar discussions and you will be soliciting participants' reactions and analyses. Let participants know your purpose in using the video so they are prepared to react appropriately. For instance, if the children's methods are to be the subject of discussion, participants should take notes while watching the video. Running times for each video segment are included in the detailed agendas, along with a brief summary of the student work presented in each video clip.

Working on the mathematics activities

The mathematics activities included in most (but not all) sessions offer work with the mathematical ideas that are addressed in the print and video cases, but at a level that is appropriate and challenging for adult learners. Often, the mathematics investigation precedes the case discussion about a particular mathematical issue; if you are adjusting the agendas to fit a different format, be sure the order of the activities is appropriate.

Sometimes participants are uncomfortable because their DMI mathematics work leaves them confused about something they thought they understood. This can be especially unsettling if it appears that the discussion for that topic is over. Reassure participants that ideas raised in one session are always revisited in another, and that future sessions will include further opportunities to work on the mathematics issues they find confusing, troubling, or puzzling.

When mental math activities are part of a session, several possible problems are provided. Depending on the amount of discussion in your group, you may have time for only one or two of these. Don't feel you must include every problem; instead, consider the purpose of the mental math exercise in the context of that particular session. Is the purpose to prepare participants for viewing a video case? Is it to have participants become familiar with a type of problem they will be reading about? Is it an opportunity for them to develop their own mathematics? Is it preparation for another mathematics activity that follows? The purpose of the mental math exercise in the session and the reactions of your participants will help you decide how many problems to present.

Exploring innovative curricular materials

As part of the final two sessions of each seminar, participants examine activities drawn from one of several elementary mathematics curricula. Working in small groups, participants familiarize themselves with the activities and discuss how they would use the material to support their students' thinking. The content of the lessons suggested for this study is related to the mathematical issues addressed in earlier sessions of the seminar.

Suggestions include activities from *Everyday Mathematics* (Everyday Learning), *Investigations in Number, Data, and Space®* (Dale Seymour), *MathLand* (Creative Publications), *Math Trailblazers* (Kendall/Hunt), and replacement units and other resources from Math Solutions Publications.

If you are working in or with a school system that has adopted one of these innovative curricula, it will be beneficial for your group to study the suggested activities from that curriculum. If your system is in the process of choosing a curriculum, you may want to explore all the possibilities. If your system already has an established curriculum other than those listed, you might look for related activities to explore in that resource.

The curriculum activities are *not* included in this facilitator's guide; facilitators will need to locate the relevant material. An effort was made to suggest activities that require minimal preparation time for facilitators and that use manipulative materials commonly available in elementary schools. The activity lists appear with the agendas for Sessions 7 and 8; if you anticipate needing extra time to obtain the activities you want your group to explore, turn to these lists early to begin preparing for those sessions.

Reading and discussing the research highlights

The last chapter of the casebook for *Building a System of Tens* is an essay describing research findings related to the mathematical issues raised by the cases. Throughout this essay, the research results are explicated with examples from those cases. Reading and discussing the essay allows participants to consider the overall themes of the casebook and to place the issues raised in individual cases in a broader perspective.

The spirit of inquiry fostered in the case discussions should also be applied to the research essay. That is, participants should feel free to question and challenge the ideas put forward and to compare these ideas with their own experiences. At the same time, they should also be encouraged to challenge their own assumptions and beliefs in light of the research findings.

Discussing portfolio assignments

In addition to their reading assignments in the casebook, participants are expected to complete writing assignments for their portfolios. Some assignments ask teachers to reflect on their learning in the seminar or to discuss implications of that learning for their teaching practice. Through other assignments, participants investigate the thinking of their *own* students: by collecting and analyzing samples of their students' work; by planning, conducting, and analyzing mathematical interviews; and by writing their own "cases." When appropriate, seminar time is allotted for discussion and analysis of participants' written work.

At the beginning and end of the *Building a System of Tens* seminar, participants bring in samples of their students' work. This activity serves a dual purpose. First, it provides a forum for participants to discuss the mathematical understandings of their students with other teachers. As the teachers

work in small groups, examining the student work and sharing their assessments, the discussion fosters a kind of collegial interaction that is integral to a successful DMI seminar and is, at the same time, likely to be a new experience for many teachers. This assignment also serves as a tool for reflection, offering participants the opportunity to track their changing views from the beginning to the end of the seminar.

At one point during the seminar on *Building a System of Tens*, participants are asked to conduct interviews with individual children. Through these interviews, teachers can explore the way an individual student thinks about the mathematical ideas addressed in the seminar. Many teachers are surprised by the thinking of the students who are described in the casebook. Sometimes participants will say, "My students don't act like the students in the cases," or "My students don't think this way." Other teachers may add that they don't have time to work with just one student. You can build on comments like these, suggesting that participants approach the interview as an opportunity to listen to the mathematical sense-making of one particular child. In general, teachers have had little experience interacting with students in this way. Tell participants explicitly that the interview is *not* a tutorial or a teaching activity for the child; rather, the purpose of the interview is for the teacher to understand the mathematical thinking of the student interviewee.

Toward the end of the seminar on *Building a System of Tens*, participants are asked to write cases based on their own classroom experiences. Even though teachers often say they feel isolated and want more interaction with their colleagues, this activity can make some participants anxious. It is important to establish that the discussions of one another's cases are not critiques of any particular teacher's practice or writing, but rather opportunities for the group to examine the mathematical thinking of the students. To emphasize this focus on the children's mathematics, the agendas suggest that participants meet in small groups to read each other's cases before starting any discussion. As participants become more familiar with the process of case writing, they grow in their ability to use this assignment to deepen their own thinking. When they first begin, teachers may be uncomfortable sharing what went wrong in their lessons or owning up to being confused by their own students. Encourage participants to use the writing of cases as a way to work on something they are trying to figure out. Point out that when they bring their cases to the seminar, they will have a chance to share them and hear the reactions of like-minded colleagues.

Using exit cards

The portfolio assignments give facilitators a sense of how individual participants are engaging with the ideas of the seminar, but there is usually a time lag between when they are written and when facilitators read them. Therefore, the DMI agendas allot five minutes at the end of each session for participants to provide more immediate feedback using "exit cards."

Facilitators have found it effective to choose two or three prompts for each session to guide participant responses. These can be written on easel paper or read aloud. Passing out an index card to each participant just before posting or reading the prompts helps make clear that this is *not* an optional activity, but rather an important conclusion to every session. The prompts might be of a general nature:

How is the seminar going for you?

What would you like to share about this session?

What questions is this seminar raising for you?

We have been working in small groups for a few sessions. How is that going?

Is there anything else you'd like to tell me?

Or they might be tailored to activities in a specific session:

Explain one reaction you had to the video clips we saw.

How did it feel to have a case that you wrote discussed?

What mathematical question did this activity raise for you?

Explain something you're thinking about from the case discussion.

What are you getting from the mental math activities?

Preparation for the seminar

Participants in the DMI seminar *Building a System of Tens* are expected to prepare some written work and to read the first set of cases before the first seminar session. The following letter is a model of how you might introduce participants to the seminar and explain their pre-seminar assignments. You will need to modify the letter to suit your circumstances, inserting the appropriate meeting dates, times, and locations. Along with your letter, include a copy of the first Homework sheet (page 25) and, if participants have not already received the materials, the casebook for *Building a System of Tens*.

Introductory Letter to Participants

Date _____

Dear Colleague,

We are excited that you have agreed to participate in one of the seminars offered by [sponsor, location, date, times _____].

In the Developing Mathematical Ideas (DMI) seminar sessions, you will have an opportunity to explore the mathematics ideas of the elementary curriculum, to analyze children's mathematical thinking as they encounter these ideas, to examine lessons from innovative curricula, and to read and discuss current research in mathematics education. The seminar is organized around a series of cases, written by teachers, describing events that occurred during their mathematics lessons. These brief narratives capture both student dialogue and teacher analysis.

In the first DMI seminar on Number and Operations, these cases address the topic *Building a System of Tens*. Through reading and discussing the cases and working on mathematical problems, you will consider the ideas underlying the base ten number system that affect learning to count, performing operations with multidigit numbers, and working with decimals. The introduction to the casebook for *Building a System of Tens* contains a more detailed account of the mathematical themes.

A second DMI seminar in Number and Operations, using the casebook *Making Meaning for Operations,* examines the four basic operations, first with whole numbers and then with fractions.

Seminar assignments will include reading cases and articles about current research in mathematics education, as well as writing short papers. Throughout the seminar, you will be keeping a portfolio of your written assignments and other material of interest to you. We will discuss the process of maintaining a portfolio at our first meeting.

Enclosed, you will find a sheet describing your first written portfolio assignment and a reading assignment that you should do before our first session. Both your written work and the reading will be discussed extensively at our first meeting.

Please call _____ if you have any questions.

Sincerely,

Homework

In the Developing Mathematical Ideas seminar, we will explore the way children engage with the topics of the elementary mathematics curriculum. Part of the first class session will be devoted to discussion of the mathematical goals we have for our students. In preparation for this discussion, please complete the following assignment.

Portfolio assignment: Children's work samples

Collect work samples from three children. Choose one whose work you think is strong and two whose work is not so strong. Explain why the first sample satisfies you. What is your analysis of the other two? What are your learning goals for each of the three children?

Please bring three copies of the work samples and your written analysis to our first session.

Reading assignment: Casebook chapter 1

In the casebook for *Building a System of Tens*, read chapter 1, including the introductory text as well as cases 1–4. As you read, think about the questions raised in the chapter introduction.

Children's Algorithms for Adding and Subtracting Two-Digit Numbers

---

Preparation and Materials

- ### Background

  Read "Maxine's Journal" through Session 1, pp. 108–118.

  Read the agenda for Session 1.

- ### Orientation

  Duplicate and review the two portfolio handouts, "The Portfolio Process," p. 33, and "Portfolio Cover Sheet," pp. 34–35.

- ### Discussion of children's work samples

  Determine grade-level discussion groups of three.

- ### Case discussion

  Read the casebook, chapter 1.

  Duplicate and review "Focus Questions" for chapter 1, p. 36.

  Determine pairs for initial small-group discussion.

- ### Math activity

  Duplicate the three sheets of number cards, pp. 39–41, on card stock. Cut apart to make 44-card decks. Make enough so each pair of participants has one deck.

  Duplicate "Math Activity: Close to 100," p. 37, and "Close to 100 Score Sheet," p. 38.

  Practice playing "Close to 100."

  Determine pairs for playing the game.

- ### Viewing the video

  Obtain a video playback machine.

  On the DMI Tape *Building a System of Tens*, locate and preview the Session 1 segment (3 minutes).

  Review the video summary, p. 31.

- ### Homework

  Duplicate "Homework" sheet for Session 1, p. 42.

Agenda

Orientation

Dedicate the first few minutes to a statement of welcome and a brief overview of the agenda for this session. Ask participants to introduce themselves. Depending on the size and composition of the group, participants might also tell the grade they teach and the name of their school.

Remind the group of the letter they received describing the two Developing Mathematical Ideas (DMI) seminars on Number and Operations: Part 1, *Building a System of Tens*, and Part 2, *Making Meaning for Operations*. Use this opportunity to comment on the K–6 nature of the materials. Entertain any questions about the seminar. Establish procedures for absences from class.

Distribute the handouts "The Portfolio Process" and "Portfolio Cover Sheet." When everyone has read these, answer questions about the portfolios. The participants' portfolios will be used to hold all their assignments for the two Number and Operations seminars, as well as any additional items that participants may choose to include. Have participants write their name and the grade level they are teaching at the top of the first sheet. Explain that they have already completed the first written assignment in their preparations for this session. Remind them to fill in the date of completion for this assignment. The blank spaces in the chart are for any additional items they choose to keep in their portfolio. **Note:** If you will be writing responses to participants' assignments, your responses should also be kept in the portfolios.

Sharing children's work samples

Assign people to grade-level groups of three and have them share the children's work samples and their analyses. Remind them that they will have 30 minutes for this activity, so they can plan about 10 minutes per person. Sit in and listen to each small group for some time; this gives you a flavor of all the discussions and also communicates to the participants that you are interested in their ideas.

Mental math

You might introduce this activity by reminding the participants that they have read about students performing "mental math" in the cases. Explain that you are going to ask them to do some math problems mentally, that is, without doing any written calculations. Ask them to pay attention to *how* they are working on the problem, because you will be asking them to share their methods. Even though they will be performing the computations mentally you might want to write the problems on an overhead or easel. Say the problems one at a time and ask people to share their methods after each one. Write out the solution methods on an easel pad or overhead transparency so participants can examine the variety of solution methods. Here are three problems you might use:

$$57 + 24 \qquad 86 - 32 \qquad 83 - 56$$

While some people might break the numbers apart in ways that are similar to those of the children described in the cases, others might be imagining a paper on which they mentally "write" the traditional steps. It is important that every person's method be valued and accepted during the whole-group discussion.

Break   (15 minutes)

Case discussion   (60 minutes)

Pairs, 20 minutes

Groups of four, 15 minutes

Whole group, 25 minutes

The four cases in chapter 1 illustrate children's various strategies for adding and subtracting multidigit numbers. In small groups, the participants will be looking carefully at the strategies used by children in the first two cases and then discussing the logic behind each strategy: What must the children already understand in order to devise these strategies?

Group participants in pairs and distribute "Focus Questions" for chapter 1. Announce that they will have 20 minutes to discuss student strategies and an additional 15 minutes to address the focus questions in groups of four. Be sure to acknowledge that 20 minutes may not be enough time for a thorough discussion, but that it is enough time to develop a sense of the issues.

At the end of 20 minutes, combine partnerships into groups of four. After 10 minutes, remind them that you will ask them to come together as a whole group in another 5 minutes. This will allow them time to reach a stopping place in their small-group conversations.

Start the whole-group discussion by focusing on one or two student strategies. Many people find Joe's subtraction strategy (case 2, line 159) particularly challenging. Then turn the conversation to the more general question of what students need to understand in order to devise their own strategies.

After discussing the first five focus questions, invite the teachers to share their responses to question 6: "What other issues came up for you as you worked on these cases?" Because a number of topics are likely to arise, you might record them on an easel pad before having a discussion. By listing all the topics, you are able to acknowledge every teacher's contribution and also display the full range of concerns or comments raised by the cases. After the list has been generated, you can ask the group which issues they want to discuss in the remaining time. It is a good idea to keep this list for future reference. You might even suggest to participants that they will be able to add to this list of issues throughout the seminar.

Math activity (30 minutes)

Playing "Close to 100," 20 minutes

Discussion, 10 minutes

Announce that the next activity is a math game called "Close to 100." Group the participants in pairs and distribute the materials for the game: the number cards, the score sheet, and the game directions. Suggest that the group play for a while using the standard scoring method, then try the scoring variation. Let them know that after playing for about 20 minutes, there will be a 10-minute discussion of the strategies they are using.

As you observe their play, note the strategies that you see players using; this alerts you to points that are likely to be brought up during the discussion of strategies. After 15 minutes, remind the group that play will be ending in 5 minutes, and that they should play at least one round using the scoring variation if they have not already done so.

Begin the whole-group discussion by asking participants to articulate what strategies they used in playing the game and what those strategies showed them about the number system. If you observed someone using a strategy that is not described during the whole-group discussion, invite the participant to share by saying something like, "I saw [name of player] using a method that focused first on the tens. Will you explain to the group what you were doing?" This kind of prompting can help teachers develop the ability to pay attention to and articulate their own thinking process.

Toward the end of this activity, explain that the group will be working on these ideas throughout the seminar. This is particularly important if you suspect that not everyone in the group fully comprehended some points that were raised.

Viewing and discussing the video

(10 minutes)

The short (3 minute) video segment for Session 1 presents three second-grade children describing their methods for adding 48 + 25. While the strategies are similar to those described in the written cases, the video offers the opportunity to listen to children present their ideas in their own voices. Play the video segment straight through; this will allow participants to form images of children sharing their thinking. At the conclusion of the video, solicit participants' reactions to what they have seen. You might explain that in the next session, they will be discussing video clips in more detail. Thus, while in this segment we simply see Stacey solving an addition problem by counting by ones, the Session 2 segment will provide opportunities to consider such student methods more fully.

Exit cards and homework

(5 minutes)

Explain to participants that you will be asking for their feedback on the seminar during the last 5 minutes of each session. Post the questions you have chosen for this session and distribute index cards for participant responses. Ask them to sign their exit cards so that you can get to know their individual interests and concerns. Distribute the Session 1 "Homework" sheet as participants leave the seminar.

Video Summary

Building a System of Tens, Session 1

To convey images of children sharing their thinking as they devise their own addition strategies, this 3-minute video segment looks into a second-grade classroom where students have been working on the following problem: "Kira has 48 cents in her pocket. Her big brother gave her 25 cents for running an errand. Now how much does she have?"

$$48 + 25$$

Elthea

She goes to the board to show how she decomposes the numbers 48 and 25 to add them in three steps.

$$40 + 20 = 60$$
$$60 + 8 = 68$$
$$68 + 5 = 73$$

James

James breaks apart only the 25, adding first the 20 and then the extra 5, itself broken into 2 and 3.

48 + 20 = 68

68 + 2 (FROM THE 5) = 70

70 + 3 (FROM THE 5) = 73

Stacey

Stacey demonstrates on the class hundreds chart that she adds by counting up by ones.

I started from 48 (*points to 48*) and then I counted 25 (*she points to each number in turn as she counts*) and ended up with 73.

The Portfolio Process

As participants in the DMI seminar *Building a System of Tens*, you will be working together to explore the way children develop mathematical ideas. You will be reading and discussing cases from other teachers' classrooms, but you will also be examining your own students' understandings and thinking about your own teaching practice. In fact, you have already begun this process by analyzing samples of your students' work.

Periodically throughout the seminar, you will be writing reflective papers about your experiences. Some of these assignments will be the basis for group discussion; other assignments will be a way of communicating with the seminar facilitator. In all cases, the assignments are designed to stimulate your thinking.

Please collect your written homework assignments in a portfolio, along with all facilitator responses to your assignments. This portfolio will be a record of your work in the seminar and will also serve as a tool for reflection. You are invited to add other material of interest to the portfolio. For example, you might include a sample of student work that surprised or pleased you, a description of a class discussion that was intriguing, or an interaction with a child that was particularly satisfying. Use the portfolio cover sheet to date and describe each entry. Please include a note explaining why you have selected each item that is not homework.

At several points during the seminar, you will review your portfolio and reflect on its contents.

SESSION 1

B U I L D I N G   A   S Y S T E M   O F   T E N S

Name_____   Grade level taught _____

Portfolio Cover Sheet

Please indicate the date each item goes into your portfolio. When you add material that is not a seminar assignment, write a brief description of it. You are not required to fill in every line.

Number and Operations, Part 1: Building a System of Tens

Date	Portfolio Assignments and Other Items
	Preparation: Children's Work Samples
	Session 1: Expectations for This Seminar
	Session 2: Thinking About Base Ten
	Session 3: Doing a Student Interview
	Session 4: Invented Strategies vs. Traditional Algorithms
	Session 5: Changes in Your Classroom
	Session 6: Reflecting on the Cases
	Session 7: A Case from Your Class
	Session 8: More Children's Work Samples

B U I L D I N G   A   S Y S T E M   O F   T E N S

Number and Operations, Part 2: Making Meaning for Operations

Date	Portfolio Assignments and Other Items
	Preparation: More Children's Work Samples*
	Session 1: Writing Another Case
	Session 2: Thoughts on Teaching Math
	Session 3: Doing Another Student Interview
	Session 4: Thoughts About the Four Operations
	Session 5: A Third Case from Your Classroom
	Session 6: Work Samples and Writing About a Case's Impact
	Session 7: Reviewing Your Portfolio

* These are the same samples collected after Session 8 of the *Building a System of Tens* seminar.

Focus Questions

Chapter 1: Cases 1–4

Refer to the question raised in the introductory text for this set of cases (page 6). Keep that question and your reactions to it in mind as you discuss the following in pairs, in small groups of four, and as a whole group.

In pairs

1. In Ann's case 1 (on addition), examine the methods presented by Janae, Tom, Bert, and Betsy. Apply their methods to this problem: 57 + 24.

2. In Ann's case 2 (on subtraction), examine the methods presented by Jason, Bert, Holly, and Joe. Apply their methods to this problem: 83 – 56.

In small groups

After comparing the children's methods, join another pair to form a group of four and discuss the following questions:

3. What is the logic behind each student's procedure?

4. What is it that children need to be able to understand about number in order to solve math problems in these ways?

5. In case 4, Emily writes that one of her second-graders, Ivan, invented a solution to a subtraction problem that was both new to her and confusing to figure out. Does Ivan's method resemble any of those presented in Ann's case 2? Emily declares this to be a time when she was learning mathematics by interacting with her students. What is your reaction to that?

6. What other issues came up for you as you worked on these cases?

Math Activity: Close to 100

Game directions

"Close to 100" is played with a deck of 44 cards—four cards each of the digits 0–9, plus four wild cards. Each pair of players needs one deck; each individual player needs a score sheet.

The point of the game is to create double-digit numbers that sum as close to 100 as possible. Each game has five rounds.

For round 1, deal six cards to each player. Players choose any four of the cards to make two double-digit numbers that, when added, come as close as possible to a total of 100. Wild cards can be assigned any value. Player record their numbers and the total on a score sheet. The player's score for the round is the difference between that total and 100. The used cards are discarded, and the two cards remaining in each hand are kept for the next round.

For rounds 2 to 5, deal out four cards to each player and repeat the steps in round 1.

At the end of five rounds, players total their scores. The player with the lowest total wins.

Scoring variation

The rules of play remain the same; only the scoring is modified. If the player's total is above 100, the score is recorded as positive. If the score is below 100, the score is recorded as negative. The player with the grand total closest to zero after five rounds is the winner.

Adapted from *Investigations in Number, Data, and Space®*, Dale Seymour Publications (1998).
This game and the related "Close to 1000" appear in several units for grades 3–5.

"Close to 100" Score Sheet

Score

Round 1: _____ + _____ = _____   _____

Round 2: _____ + _____ = _____   _____

Round 3: _____ + _____ = _____   _____

Round 4: _____ + _____ = _____   _____

Round 5: _____ + _____ = _____   _____

Total score   _____

BUILDING A SYSTEM OF TENS

Number Cards for "Close to 100"

0	0	0	0
1	1	1	1
2	2	2	2
3	3	3	3

BUILDING A SYSTEM OF TENS

Number Cards for "Close to 100"

4	4	4	4
5	5	5	5
6	6	6	6
7	7	7	7

© Education Development Center, Inc.

BUILDING A SYSTEM OF TENS

Number Cards for "Close to 100"

8	8	8	8
9	9	9	9
wild card	wild card	wild card	wild card

Homework

Portfolio assignment: Expectations for this seminar

Given their previous experiences in teacher-education courses, workshops, seminars, and projects, most teachers enter a new program with a set of particular hopes and expectations. Once the program begins, however, they frequently find that it isn't offering exactly what they expected. This might be disappointing, if they discover that the program won't meet a set of needs they had hoped it would. Or it might be exciting, if they find that the program offers new insights and opens up possibilities they had never dreamed of.

In preparation for the next seminar meeting, please write a response to the following questions:

1. What are your expectations for this seminar?

2. How did the first session compare with your expectations?

Reading assignment: Casebook chapter 2

Read chapter 2 of the casebook for *Building a System of Tens*, including both the introductory text and cases 5–10. As you read, think about the questions raised in the chapter introduction.

Recognizing and Keeping Track of Groups of 10 While Operating

Preparation and Materials

■ Background

Read "Maxine's Journal," Session 2, pp. 119–128.

Read the agenda for Session 2.

■ Viewing the video

Obtain a video playback machine.

On the DMI Tape *Building a System of Tens*, locate and preview the Session 2 segment (5 minutes, 30 seconds).

Review the video summary, p. 47.

■ Case discussion

Read the casebook, chapter 2.

Duplicate and review "Focus Questions" for chapter 2, p. 50.

Determine groups of three for small-group discussion.

Obtain base ten blocks, Cuisenaire® rods, and Unifix®, Multilink™, or any other interlocking cubes.

■ Homework

Duplicate "Homework" sheet for Session 2, p. 51.

Agenda

Introductions   (5 minutes)

Take the first few minutes to ask if there are any questions about the seminar. Review everyone's name. If the participants do not know each other, you might want to have introductions at the beginning of each session. Give a brief overview of the agenda for the session.

Viewing and discussing the video   (45 minutes)

Participants will have read six cases that present children's strategies for solving addition and subtraction problems. The video segment for Session 2 shows children working on subtraction problems with methods similar to those in the written cases; however, the video offers the added opportunity to see and hear children struggling to express their ideas and to understand the ideas of their peers. With the video, participants are able to listen to the students in real time, to hear their tone of voice, and to see the children's writing. While the written cases allow for detailed analysis, the video supplements this work by providing a visual image of the kinds of classroom scenes being described in the written cases.

The video shows five children working on two different problems: 40 – 26 and 35 – 16. Some of their strategies are similar to those presented in the written cases; others are new.

Remind the teachers that they will be talking about the written cases later in the session, but first they will be viewing a video of students working on two-digit subtraction problems.

This segment runs a total of about 6 minutes, but you should stop the tape after each strategy to review what the child has done. To enhance understanding, you can ask participants to apply each child's strategy to a new problem, such as 54 – 38 or 82 – 27. Continue to alternate these activities— watching the tape and applying the children's strategies—throughout the video segment.

Small-group case discussion   (40 minutes)

The cases in chapter 2 describe students who are working on the meaning of the tens place in the context of two-digit addition problems. As the students work on the problems, they use a variety of manipulative materials to represent number.

Teachers who have had little experience with manipulatives will need the opportunity to experiment with them before they can begin to analyze the student thinking presented in these cases. Focus question 1 provides that opportunity. If you know which teachers are new to these manipulatives, you might group them together; this way, they will be able to spend considerable time on this question without feeling the pressure to move on. If some of your participants are already comfortable with the manipulatives, suggest that they spend only a brief time on question 1 before turning to questions 2 and 3, in which they will work at understanding what the students are doing and at identifying the mathematical ideas the students are putting together.

After placing teachers in groups of three, distribute "Focus Questions" for chapter 2 and the manipulatives. Advise participants that they will have 40 minutes in these small groups. As you circulate, you may need to help participants to stay focused on the mathematics in the cases. Asking people to cite specific line numbers in the cases to back up general statements can provide this focus. It may be a new experience for people to look at wrong answers and identify the logic in them. You can refocus the conversation by asking questions such as, What is right about what this student did? or What is it that she understands? Encouraging people to act out exactly what the students did is also a helpful strategy.

Break
(15 minutes)

Whole-group case discussion
(40 minutes)

You will have to decide whether it is worthwhile to have a discussion on all three focus questions or if you prefer to concentrate on questions 2 and 3. This depends on the familiarity of your group with manipulative materials. If you want to include question 1, you might start by asking what people want to share from their work on that question.

Then turn the conversation to questions 2 and 3, the particulars of Serena and Sarah. Explain that you will gather, in columns on the easel paper, their responses to the questions "What was she confused about?" and "What did she learn?" First, consider Serena (question 2). As you record participants' statements, be sure to maintain the focus on the cases by requesting line numbers that locate the relevant text. Then turn to Sarah (question 3). Continue to gather comments from the small groups and record them in the appropriate column. Then invite teachers to think about the more general question, What are the mathematical issues that these students are working through?

Setting group norms for case discussion
(20 minutes)

The teachers have now participated in two case discussions. Explain that you are interested in having them reflect on their experiences to decide what routines the group should adopt to support productive discussion. Give people three or four minutes to think, and then ask for comments. Use this opportunity to establish some norms for case discussion. As the group generates rules, you might write them on easel paper, which can be posted and referred to during subsequent seminar sessions.

While specific comments will vary from group to group, you might try to include the following: the use of line number references to support statements, the value of paraphrasing (asking one person to repeat another person's comments), and the importance of accepting different interpretations of the same text.

Mental math
(10 minutes)

Announce that the seminar session will end with another mental math activity. Tell the teachers you will be giving them two- and three-digit computations to perform without pencil or paper. Let them know that you will ask for their strategies after each problem. Here are possible problems:

$$69 + 23 \qquad 138 + 85 \qquad 63 - 27 \qquad 132 - 85$$

If you still have time after sharing strategies for the last problem, you might ask participants to talk about what it was like to do this mental math.

Exit cards and homework
(5 minutes)

Distribute index cards and post the questions you want the group to reflect upon. Distribute the Session 2 "Homework" sheet as participants leave the seminar.

Video Summary

Building a System of Tens, Session 2

This 6-minute video segment shows second-grade students working on two subtraction problems, 40 − 26 and 36 − 18. The summary highlights the significant steps of each student's work and the teacher's questions (in italics). Students' words are not necessarily exact quotes.

40 - 26

Three students, Lisa, James, and Naillil, show us their thinking for the first subtraction problem.

Lisa

Lisa writes her process on the board.

40 - 6 = 34
34 - 20 = 14

Where did you get the 6?

I got the 6 from the 26. I separated the 26, to make it easier.

Where did the 20 come from?

The 26, too.

James

James points to a diagram he has drawn as he explains his approach.

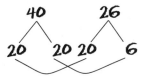

I split the 40 into 20 and 20.

I split the 26 into 20 and 6.

I minused 6 from 20 and got 14.

I knew 20 − 20 = 0.

I minused 0 from 14 and got 14.

Why did you decide to do it this way?

It makes the numbers easier.

Naillil

She has written three statements on the board.

$$26 + 4 = 30$$
$$30 + 10 = 40$$
$$4 + 10 = 14$$

I wanted to get to the closest 10, which is 30. I know I needed to plus 4 to get to 30, and 30 + 10 = 40. And I just plussed 4 and 10 equals 14.

Why did you add these two numbers together?

. . . I had to know which numbers I plussed on. I thought of 26 marbles in front of me. Kira had 40. I needed to get to 40. I didn't just go 14 because I didn't know it was 14.

I broke little numbers in pieces to get to 40.

---

35 − 16

Two students, Glen and Becky, explain their strategies for this second problem.

Glen

He reads from his paper.

I wrote 35 − 16. And then 6 minus 5 equals negative 1. *(Does he mean 5 minus 6?)*

$$30 - 10 = 20$$
$$20 - 1 = 19$$

The teacher writes his problem vertically on the board to clarify.

$$
\begin{array}{r}
35 \\
- 16 \\
\hline
\end{array}
20 - 1 = 19
$$

Becky

Becky writes the same problem on the board.

$$\begin{array}{r} 35 \\ -\ 16 \\ \hline 20 \end{array}$$

Now can you explain what you did?

> What I did was I wrote the numbers [one above the other]. Five take away 6 is 0, and 3 take away 1 is 2. So that's 20.

Can you tell me how you know that 5 minus 6 equals 0?

> Because 6 is more than 5. If it's more than 5, it has to be 0 because . . . it can only equal something above 0 if it's less than the number. Five is less than 6.

Focus Questions

Chapter 2: Cases 5–10

Refer to the questions raised in the introductory text for these cases (page 20). Keep those questions and your reactions to them in mind as you discuss these focus questions.

In cases 5–10, we see several students who used manipulatives to represent number. In case 5, Serena used base ten blocks. In case 6, Sarah used Unifix cubes. In case 8, Julie used Cuisenaire rods.

1. Take a set of each kind of manipulative and figure out how it can be used to represent number. Demonstrate how the different materials can be used to model 35 + 26 = 61 and 72 – 34 = 38.

2. Now turn to Serena (case 5, line 56). Act out what she did with the blocks. What was she confused about? What did she understand? What did she learn?

3. Consider Sarah (case 6, line 90). Act out what she did with the cubes. What was she confused about? What did she understand? What did she learn?

4. In case 10 (line 486), we see Tania at work on a coin-counting problem, using a combination of tally marks and numbers.

    a. What is *your* answer to the question Kara raises: "What role do the tally marks play for a child in this kind of counting?"

    b. What do you see that Tania understands? What is she confused about?

Homework

Portfolio assignment: Thinking about base ten

For the first two sessions of this seminar, you have been exploring issues about the base ten structure of the number system in two ways: (1) through examining classroom episodes that bring aspects of children's thinking to light, and (2) through doing mathematics activities yourself and reflecting on your own strategies and insights.

For the next session, please respond in writing to the following:

1. What ideas about numbers and the base ten number system have been highlighted for you by these readings, videos, discussions, and activities?

2. What questions do you have?

Reading assignment: Casebook chapter 3

Read chapter 3 of the casebook for *Building a System of Tens*, including both the introductory text and cases 11–15. As you read, think about the questions raised in the chapter introduction.

Written Numerals and the Structure of Tens and Ones

Preparation and Materials

■ Background

Read "Maxine's Journal," Session 3, pp. 129–135.

Read the agenda for Session 3.

■ Case discussion

Read the casebook, chapter 3.

Duplicate and review "Focus Questions" for chapter 3, p. 58.

Determine pairs for small-group discussion.

Obtain base ten blocks, interlocking cubes, Cuisenaire rods, and counters.

■ Viewing the video

Obtain a video playback machine.

On the DMI Tape *Building a System of Tens*, locate and preview the Session 3 segment (11 minutes, 30 seconds).

Review the video summary, p. 56.

■ Math interview planning

Determine grade-level groups of three for planning the math interviews.

Duplicate "Sample Interview Write-up," pp. 59–61.

Read ahead in "Maxine's Journal," Session 4, pp. 136–138, for an idea of what to anticipate with these interviews.

■ Homework

Duplicate "Homework" sheet for Session 3, p. 62.

Agenda

Case discussion

(70 minutes)

Pairs, 30 minutes

Whole group, 40 minutes

The cases in chapter 3 present students' thinking about the spoken and written number systems and the connections between them. In both small-group and whole-group discussions, the teachers work to understand the logic behind what appears to be, on the surface, incorrect student thinking. For instance, participants will explore why someone might think "5 and 10" is the number after 59, or why someone would write 1005 for *one hundred and five.*

Distribute "Focus Questions" for chapter 3. Tell participants they will have 30 minutes to work on the focus questions with their partners.

Solicit participants' comments on each of the focus questions during the first 30 minutes of whole-group discussion. Then use the last 10 minutes to pose the more general question, "What are you noticing about the number system by examining these cases?" In order to set the tone for the interview assignment, you might also want to ask, "What questions does this work raise for you about the way children make sense of our number system?"

Viewing and discussing the video

(30 minutes)

View the video, 12 minutes

Discuss the mathematics, 18 minutes

Distribute the Session 3 "Homework" sheet, which describes the math interview that participants will conduct in preparation for Session 4. You might distribute "Sample Interview Write-up" at this time as well. Let the teachers know that the rest of this seminar session will be devoted to preparation for their own math interview. They will view a videotaped interview for two purposes: first, to explore the child's mathematical ideas, and second, to examine the way the interviewer worked with the child. Advise teachers to take notes while viewing the tape so they will be able to discuss both aspects of the interview.

After viewing the tape, begin the discussion with a general question about the mathematics in the video: What is the mathematics content that Chris is working on? Then ask participants to analyze the boy's mathematical understandings. Record participants' comments on easel paper under two headings, "Does understand" and "Does *not* understand." As points are offered, it may be necessary to ask follow-up questions so that the comments are specific rather than vague. When teachers offer a point, ask them to refer to something specific that the child says or does that provides evidence for the statement. This process helps ground the discussion and keeps participants focused on the specifics of the interview. As the discussion proceeds, you might find it useful to add a third heading, "What we don't know."

Break
(15 minutes)

Examining the interview process
(20 minutes)

Turn the attention of the group to the interview process by asking, "What did you notice about the way the interviewer worked with Chris that will be helpful as you think about conducting a similar interview?" Some groups may ask to view a portion of the interview a second time with this question in mind, while others may feel ready for this discussion after one viewing. Possible points to discuss:

- reacting to the child's responses in the same way whether they are correct or incorrect

- asking probing rather than leading questions

- starting with a math problem well within the child's ability, to put him or her at ease

- asking follow-up questions specifically related to what the child said

In general, reinforce that a math interview is an opportunity for the interviewer to learn about the child's thinking, rather than to teach the child.

Planning the math interview
(40 minutes)

Small groups, 25 minutes

Whole group, 15 minutes

Teachers meet in grade-level groups to plan questions and tasks for their math interviews. Each group will choose a mathematical area related to the issues raised in the seminar thus far and then design mathematical tasks and questions that they will each ask in their interviews. Alert the participants that the questions provide merely a starting point for the interview, and that each interviewer should follow the logic of the child being interviewed. After grade-level groups have decided on their plans, bring the whole group together to share briefly what they are planning.

You might discuss "Sample Interview Write-up" as a whole group. This kind of writing may be new for the teachers. Clarify that their write-up should be not a verbatim account of what they and the student said, but rather a description of what they learned about how the child understands a particular math idea. Quotes from the interview can be used as supporting evidence, but the interview write-up should not be thought of as a transcript.

Exit cards and homework
(5 minutes)

Distribute index cards and post the questions you want the group to reflect upon. Remind participants that they already have their homework assignment, to be completed before Session 4: to conduct and write up a math interview with a student, and to read chapter 4 of the casebook.

Video Summary

Building a System of Tens, Session 3

This 12-minute video segment, "Interview with a Six-Year-Old," demonstrates a math interview with a child named Chris, shortly before he starts first grade. The interview is conducted by Jill Bodner Lester.

The interview begins with Jill asking Chris to count. Chris successfully counts by ones. Jill stops him when he reaches 61.

In the next sequence Jill asks Chris, "What is the biggest number that you know?" Chris first says "200, no, 100," and writes this. He then asks whether she means the biggest number he can count to, or the biggest number that he *knows.* He says he can count to 100. When she requests the biggest number that he "knows," Chris mentions a thousand and a million, and says he knows how to write a thousand. Jill suggests that he do that. After he has written 1000, Jill asks him how he knows it is a thousand and Chris responds by saying that it has three zeros. When Jill asks if a thousand always has three zeros, Chris replies no, that sometimes it has numbers like 5 or 6 or 10. This leads to a conversation about where to place the 5 to make the number one thousand and five (1005).

In the next portion of the interview, Jill starts counting and asks Chris to continue from where she leaves off. She uses the following sequences as prompts: 5, 6, 7; then 26, 27, 28; then 47, 48, 49; and finally 105, 106, 107. He is able to continue in each instance.

Next Jill asks Chris to write particular numbers as she says them: 8, 9, 13, 19, 24, 31, 42, 100, 102, 110. He writes some digits backwards, and corrects his backward 4.

In the final sequence of the interview, Jill and Chris have a conversation about how to write the multidigit numbers one hundred and two (102) and one hundred and ten (110).

Focus Questions

Chapter 3: Cases 11–15

Refer to the questions raised in the introductory text for these cases (page 44). Keep those questions and your reactions to them in mind as you discuss the following with a partner and later with the whole group.

1. Turn to Dawn's case 11 and study Andrew. Why does it make sense to him to have "5 and 10" follow 59? What does he understand? What is he missing?

2. In Danielle's case 15, the children came up with many ways to write "one hundred ninety-five." What sense do you see in each one?

3. In Muriel's case 14, the children talk about different kinds of zeros. Explain what they mean by this.

4. Turn to Donna's case 12. Use cubes or counters to do the bean-counting activity Donna describes. What mathematics is highlighted as you do this work?

B U I L D I N G   A   S Y S T E M   O F   T E N S

Sample Interview Write-up

100s, place value, and Nick

We had just finished working on two-digit subtraction and addition. I decided to ask my class to write three-digit numbers because I wanted to see what they would do with the hundreds now that they were familiar with the tens and the ones.

I read ten numbers aloud and asked them each to show the number. They could show it with cubes, write it as a number, or write it in words. These were the numbers: 251, 430, 102, 333, 707, 111, 507, 990, 717, 405.

After class was over, I looked at Nick's work. He had done some of the numbers with base ten blocks and some with words, but mostly he used numbers:

1.   [251]

2.   [430]   4 hundred and thirty

3.   [102]   102

4.   [333]   30033

5.   [707]   7007

6.   [111]   100 + 11= 111

7.   [507]   five hundred seven

8.   [990]   900090

9.   [717]   7000017

10. [405]

BUILDING A SYSTEM OF TENS

I was interested in what Nick had done, so I decided to ask him about his work and to do my interview with him. I started by asking him to show me all the different ways he could make the number 132. These were his responses:

1. 132

2. 100 + 32 = 132

3. 10032

4. 100032

5. 1000032

6. 1032

7. 10000032

8. 100000032

9.

10. one hundred thirty two

11. 1 + 1 + 1 + 1 + 1 + 1 + 1 + 1 + 1 + 1 + 1 + 1 + . . . (After about 50, I told him he didn't have to finish.)

I was interested that, with the first group of numbers, he wrote 102 correctly but not 333, 707, 990, or 717. He thought he needed zeros to show 100, and 102 has a zero. I asked him why he had two, three, or four zeros for some numbers. He didn't think it mattered how many zeros he wrote, because "zero plus anything is zero."

Again I was fascinated with his zeros in his ways of writing 132. Again, he told me that they all meant 100 because, "no matter how many zeros you put after 100, it's still 100." This was the first time I had seen this particular zero error.

I then asked Nick to do a three-digit addition problem, which he completed as follows:

$$\begin{array}{r} 128 \\ + 133 \\ \hline 2511 \end{array}$$

B U I L D I N G   A   S Y S T E M   O F   T E N S

He read his answer as "25 hundred and 11." I then had him show me the problem with base ten blocks, which he arranged like this:

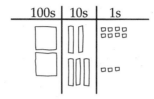

He looked at his answer and said he had 11 ones, 5 tens, and 2 hundreds. I asked him if he remembered what we did with two-digit addition; he did remember that we had traded ten ones for a tens rod. He was then able to get the answer, 261. I tried one more:

$$\begin{array}{r} 127 \\ + \ 98 \\ \hline \end{array}$$

This time his answer was 295. I had him show me with the blocks again:

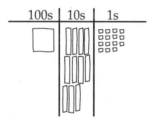

He did trade 10 ones for a tens rod, so then he had 1 hundred block, 12 tens rods, and 5 ones. On his own he traded 10 tens rods for another hundred block. I asked him how he knew to do this and he said, "I know counting to 10 ten times is 100." He ultimately wrote the answer 225.

As I reflect on Nick's work, I see that he has right and wrong ideas all tangled up. He's right when he writes 111 as 100 + 11. He says something important that is true about zero: "Zero added to a number doesn't change the number." Yet he uses that statement to explain that 10032, 100032, and 100032 all mean the same thing, and that's wrong. He is able to use what he knows about adding two-digit numbers to reason correctly about working with three-digit numbers. So I find his work intriguing. I feel he is well on his way to understanding the hundreds place value, but still has some things to figure out. I think that what he needs is more experiences with numbers and problems of this type.

Homework

Portfolio assignment: Doing a student interview

One major thread of this seminar is the examination of the ways children think as they build an understanding of the number system. One way to learn about children's thinking is to listen carefully to individuals as they articulate their own thoughts while doing mathematical tasks.

The math interview is one strategy for obtaining evidence about children's thinking. Doing interviews helps you develop a sense of the kinds of response that most students at a certain age or grade might give. An interview also helps you delve into the thinking of an individual child, to get underneath the surface of the child's responses to better understand his or her reasoning. Your assignment for the next session will be to plan, conduct, and write about an interview with a student.

In your interview, explore the student's ideas about the number system, drawing on what we have done in this seminar. Ask the student to perform some tasks, which might include questions about reading and writing numbers, counting, adding, or subtracting. You might want to use activities or questions from the cases we have read, from the videotapes we have watched, or from activities we have done together in class. These will give you a place to start, but feel free to add your own tasks and questions.

Although you will need to plan questions and tasks in advance, you will also need to follow carefully what the student does and says during the interview, so that you can follow up with questions or problems that seem appropriate. Keep in mind that your job in the interview is to find out as much as you can about the student's ideas, *not* to try to teach the student anything. Tape-record the interview so you will be able to listen to it later.

Include the following in your write-up: what questions you planned to investigate, what tasks you chose, what happened during the interview, what you learned (or didn't learn) about the student's ideas, what surprised you or confused you, what questions you are left with, and what you learned from conducting this kind of interview. Give enough information so that the reader can understand the highlights of what happened and what you learned.

Reading assignment: Casebook chapter 4

Read chapter 4 in the casebook for *Building a System of Tens,* including both the introductory text and cases 16–17. As you read, think about the questions raised in the chapter introduction.

More on Addition and Subtraction of Two-Digit Numbers

Preparation and Materials

- ### Background

    Read "Maxine's Journal," Session 4, pp. 136–141.

    Read the agenda for Session 4.

- ### Discussion of interviews

    Plan for the same grade-level group assignments as in Session 3.

- ### Case discussion

    Read the casebook, chapter 4.

    Duplicate and review "Focus Questions" for chapter 4, p. 70.

    Determine pairs for small-group discussion.

    Obtain base ten blocks, interlocking cubes, and Cuisenaire rods.

- ### Viewing the video

    Obtain a video playback machine.

    On the DMI Tape *Building a System of Tens,* locate and preview the Session 4 segment (23 minutes, 15 seconds).

    Review the video summary, p. 66.

- ### Homework

    Duplicate "Homework" sheet for Session 4, p. 71.

Agenda

Discussion of interviews (50 minutes)

Small groups, 30 minutes

Whole groups, 20 minutes

To share what they learned, have teachers return to the same small groups in which they planned their interviews. Remind them that they will have 30 minutes for this sharing and they should be aware of using the time equitably. As you listen in to each group, take note of the points that are being raised so that you can refer to them as you lead the whole-group discussion.

Begin the whole-group discussion by asking each group to offer a comment of interest from its discussion.

Some teachers may have been uncomfortable as they became aware of a child's misunderstandings and may be wondering what they are supposed to do now that they have this information. Other teachers may begin to realize that it is likely that many of their students, now and in the past, have had the same confusions, but that they (the teachers) never realized it before. For these reasons, the interview assignment and this discussion can become emotional.

Case discussion in pairs (30 minutes)

The cases in chapter 4 have a different character from those in the first three chapters because they are written by a single teacher in two different years. Through the mathematics of these cases, participants revisit ideas first presented in chapter 1 regarding students' own procedures for addition and subtraction. This chapter can help participants clarify and solidify their own methods for combining and breaking apart numbers. Focus questions 1 and 2 provide a means for teachers to work on the mathematics for themselves; question 3 raises a more general mathematical principle.

The cases also raise a somewhat charged issue—the role of the historically taught algorithms in elementary-school mathematics. Focus question 4 addresses this matter. Although the DMI developers do not take a position on this issue, teacher-writers in the casebook take various positions. We believe it is important for teachers to think about and talk about the role of the historically taught algorithms as they make decisions about their own teaching practice.

Distribute "Focus Questions" for chapter 4 to each pair of teachers and remind them that they will have 30 minutes to work on these. Advise participants that the whole-group discussion of these two cases will take place after you have viewed a video clip that presents some of the same issues.

Break (15 minutes)

Viewing the video (25 minutes)

This longer narrated video segment shows children creating their own procedures for mathematics problems; it also includes interviews with teachers describing their reactions to the children's methods. While the video offers a coherent articulation of the ideas explored in the first four seminar sessions, it may present images of classrooms that are far from the participants' experiences; thus, the coherence may not be immediately comprehended.

Whole-group discussion of the video and print cases (45 minutes)

You can begin the whole-group discussion by referring to focus question 3 or 4, or by asking, "What questions have these cases, both in the casebook and on the video, raised for you?"

Mental math (10 minutes)

Remind participants of the mental mathematics they did earlier in the seminar. Suggest that they might do these problems by looking for ways to break apart numbers. As before, have a discussion of strategies for each problem before going on to the next. First, begin with examples from addition and subtraction:

$69 + 23$ $\qquad$ $132 - 85$

Then move to multiplication, which is the topic of the next set of cases:

29×6 $\qquad$ 16×3 $\qquad$ 153×2

Again, discuss participants' different approaches after each problem.

Exit cards and homework (5 minutes)

Distribute index cards and post the questions for participant reflection. Hand out the Session 4 "Homework" sheet as participants leave the seminar. For the reading assignment, note that the term *array* is used in the next set of cases. You might explain what this term means so that everyone will read the next set of cases with the shared understanding that *array* indicates a rectangular arrangement. Refer to "Maxine's Journal," p. 141, to see how she handled this.

Video Summary

Building a System of Tens, Session 4

This narrated 23-minute video segment, "Addition and Subtraction," presents scenes from a variety of classrooms in which students from kindergarten through fourth grade are working on addition and subtraction problems. It also includes commentary by four of the classroom teachers.

The video begins with an introduction by the narrator followed by three short, focused clips. In the first, a kindergarten class uses counting to see how many children are in the class. In the next, students in another kindergarten class are counting dots in a large numeral 10 and notice that both 6 + 4 and 5 + 5 make 10. In the third clip, we see two second-grade girls using colored cubes they have counted out to work on the problem 35 – 18.

In the next sequence, a second grader, Anthony, explains and demonstrates how many moves it takes to get from 38 to 65 on the hundreds chart. This is followed by comments from his teacher, Carol Walker, on the boy's growing ability to work with ones and tens.

During a series of short clips of students at work, the narrator outlines the characteristics of a classroom in which children are developing strategies based on sound number sense.

39 – 17

The next sequence shows a second-grade teacher working to record one student's strategy for solving this problem: "Yesterday at the park I saw 39 pigeons. When a big dog walked by, 17 flew away. How many were still there?"

Sean

After Sean confuses the teacher with his explanation, they start over and she writes each step on the board as he explains what he did.

$$39 - 17$$
$$17 = 9 + 8$$
$$39 - 9 = 30$$
$$30 - 8 = 22$$

This sequence concludes with comments by the teacher, Rose Christiansen, explaining how she figured out what he was doing, and how she deals with student thinking in her class.

48 + 25

Another second grader, Victoria, presents her strategy for calculating 48 + 25.

Victoria

> She writes on the board and explains her thinking.
>
> $40 + 20 = 60$
>
> I splitted the 8 into two numbers.
>
> $5 + 5 = 10$
>
> $60 + 10 = 70$
>
> $70 + 3 = 73$
>
> *Can you explain where you are getting your 5 plus 5?*
>
> I splitted the 8 into two numbers, 5 and 3.

The sequence concludes with further comments by the teacher, Rose Christiansen, on what she found when she really began listening to students' ways of thinking.

35 - 16

The next sequence presents a second-grade teacher working to record Laura's strategy for this problem: "Jake had 35 cents in his pocket. 16 cents fell out. How much money is left?" The teacher records the numbers shown as she converses with Laura.

Laura

> I took three tens.
>
> *And you put pluses between them, right?* (Laura nods.)
>
> $10 + 10 + 10$
>
> And then I put another 5.
>
> $10 + 10 + 10 + 5$
>
> *So what is this altogether?*
>
> It's 35.
>
> $10 + 10 + 10 + 5 = 35$

Then I took 4 out of the 10 . . . I mean, I took 6 out of the 10 and that left 4.

How come you took 6 out of the 10?

Because then that would make 16.

Can I use this ten then? (The teacher points to the second 10.)

Yes.

$$10 + (4 + 6) + 10 + 5$$

So you thought of this [10] as having a 4 and a 6, and you wanted to have 6 so you could take away 16?

Yes. Then I circled a 10 . . . and then I counted a 5 and a 4.

So this [another 10] gets taken away also. This [a 10 and the 6] is what fell out, and then you counted the 10 and the 5 and the 4? And that made 19?

$$10 + 5 + 4 = 19$$

This sequence concludes with comments by the teacher, Lisa Seyferth, on Laura's progress in starting to think in terms of tens instead of always ones.

$$1000 - 359$$

Next, we see the strategies fourth graders use with larger numbers when they work on the problem 1000 – 359. The teacher writes the mathematical expressions on the board (shown at left) as a fourth-grade boy explains his approach.

Fourth grader

$$1000 - 359$$

Pretend the 9 isn't there and it's a 0 . . .

You'd take away 300, leaving you with 700.

$$1000 - 300 = 700$$

Then minus 50 equals 650.

$$700 - 50 = 650$$

And then you have to put the 9 back in, so minus 9 is 641.

$$650 - 9 = 641$$

Anthony

Anthony proposes "another way" to do the same problem.

$$999 - 359 = 640$$

Why did you do that?

Because it will end up on a 0 . . . on a ten. And then just plus 1.

$$640 + 1 = 641$$

Their teacher, Helen McElroy, remarks on the unexpected subtraction of 1 from 1000 in Anthony's approach, which works so well yet was not obvious to her. She reflects that when you really listen to kids' thinking, you're going to get surprises like that.

The video concludes with a summary by the narrator and comments from the second-grade teacher, Lisa Seyferth, on the tension she experienced between teaching the way she felt she was "supposed" to, and really listening to kids' ideas.

Focus Questions

Chapter 4: Cases 16–17

Refer to the questions raised in the introductory text for these cases (page 62). Keep those questions and your reactions to them in mind as you discuss the following.

1. In case 16, Lynn presents to her class a poster with five methods for solving 38 + 25. Use those five methods to compute 46 + 37. What is the logic behind each procedure? What do you have to understand about numbers in order to make sense of each one?

2. In case 17, we see Lynn's students working to develop computational strategies for subtraction. In particular, Fiona (line 231) struggles to make sense of 37 – 19. She breaks the numbers apart but isn't sure how to combine them. What helps Fiona in this case?

3. As we look at all of the children's methods in case 17, we see that the issues in subtraction are more complex than in addition. Use an example from the case to articulate some of the differences between addition and subtraction.

4. In case 16, Lynn writes about her discomfort in presenting her students with the historically taught algorithm because they already have procedures for combining numbers that are meaningful to them. What is your reaction to her comments?

Homework

Portfolio assignment: Invented strategies vs. traditional algorithms

In the first few sessions of *Building a System of Tens*, you have seen and read about children inventing their own strategies for performing arithmetic computations. Consider your responses to the readings, the videos, and the discussions to explain your ideas about the following questions.

1. What mathematics do children need to understand in order to be able to invent their own strategies and approaches?

2. What is the relationship between these invented strategies and the traditional algorithms?

3. What questions does this work raise for you?

Reading assignment: Casebook chapter 5

Read chapter 5 in the casebook for *Building a System of Tens*, including both the introductory text and cases 18–21. As you read, consider the questions raised in the chapter introduction.

Multiplication of Multidigit Numbers

Preparation and Materials

■ Background

Read "Maxine's Journal," Session 5, pp. 142–150, and first part of Session 6, pp. 151–152.

Read the agenda for Session 5.

■ Math activity

Duplicate "Math Activity: Multidigit Multiplication," p. 79.

Obtain graph paper, base ten blocks, Cuisenaire rods, and interlocking cubes.

Work through the activity yourself.

Determine working groups of three (consider grade-level groups).

■ Viewing the video

Obtain a video playback machine.

On the DMI Tape *Building a System of Tens,* locate and preview the Session 5 segment (10 minutes, 30 seconds).

Review the video summary, p. 76.

■ Case discussion

Read the casebook, chapter 5.

Duplicate and review "Focus Questions" for chapter 5, p. 80.

Have at hand the base ten blocks, interlocking cubes, and Cuisenaire rods.

■ Homework

Duplicate "Homework" sheet for Session 5, p. 81.

Agenda

Math Activity

(70 minutes)

Small groups, 35 minutes

Whole group, 35 minutes

Up to now, the cases have focused on strategies for performing addition and subtraction calculations that involve taking numbers apart and recombining them. The math activity in this session, "Multidigit Multiplication," extends this work into multiplication. If you organize teachers in grade-level groups for this activity, teachers of primary grades will not feel they are at a disadvantage compared to teachers in the group whose curriculum includes multidigit multiplication.

Distribute the math activity sheet, telling teachers they will have 35 minutes to work in small groups. As you check in with the small groups, encourage participants to use their answer to the first task to guide their work for the second by asking them to show you the connections between their word problem and the representation they built with the manipulatives.

The 35-minute whole-group discussion should center on the comments offered by the teachers, but look for opportunities to discuss the following two points about multiplication:

First, a multiplication expression can be modeled in different ways. For instance, 16×18 might represent the situation of 16 children, each of whom has 18 lollipops. A model of this situation could involve 16 groups of 18 items, with 16 referring to the number of children and 18 referring to the number of lollipops. On the other hand, some teachers may have used an area model to represent 16×18. For instance, they may have drawn a rectangle with a length of 16 to represent the number of children and a width of 18 to represent the number of lollipops each child has. Underscoring the connections between the model and the word problem during the whole-group discussion can help participants understand that both representations are possible ways to model 16×18.

Second, like addition and subtraction, multiplication calculations can involve breaking apart and recombining numbers in various ways. Exploring why some decompositions are correct and some are not can provide fruitful discussion. Asking people to draw diagrams, make models, or provide problem situations for their work will help the group sort out these differences and determine which are correct.

The third task in the activity focuses participants' attention on three strategies that they have previously encountered as methods for performing multidigit *addition*. In the fourth task, they examine why these strategies do not hold for multiplication and determine how to modify them so that they *are* appropriate multiplication strategies. You might refer participants to Susannah's cases (cases 20 and 21); examining the logic in her students' procedures can further develop these ideas.

During the discussion of the different ways that numbers can be broken apart, you might want to introduce the term *distributive property*, or $a\,(b + c) = ab + ac$. You can refer to the numerical example and diagram for $4\,(23) = 4\,(20) + 4\,(3)$ in Lauren's case 19. Once this area model has been considered, you can ask teachers to explore the connections between it and the distributive property. If the group feels up to it, you might examine the model to see if or how it matches the traditional multiplication algorithm.

Near the end of the discussion, acknowledge that this kind of thinking about multiplication may be new to some participants. Reassure the group that you are not expecting them to understand everything they have heard discussed. Let them know that they will be continuing to work on these ideas in the case discussion.

Break
(15 minutes)

Viewing the video
(15 minutes)

Keep participants in the same small groups while you explain that they will be viewing a video of students in third grade and fifth grade working on multiplication problems. Because the following small-group and whole-group discussions will draw on material from both the video and the print cases, suggest that participants take notes during the video.

Small-group case discussion
(30 minutes)

Distribute "Focus Questions" for chapter 5 to each small group. Announce that they will have 30 minutes to work on the questions about the print cases and to discuss the video. Let participants know that they likely will not have time to explore all of the focus questions.

Whole-group case discussion

(30 minutes)

When the group is comfortable with the mathematics of the various approaches, focus the whole-group discussion on the procedures devised by Jen (in case 18) and Michael (in case 20), as addressed in focus questions 2 and 3. Then turn the conversation to the more general question, What do these strategies highlight about multiplication?

Mental math

(15 minutes)

Conclude the session with another mental math activity. Take one problem at a time, giving people the chance to explain their strategies. While participants should compute the problems mentally, plan to record their strategies on easel paper. If you use the problems 20×23, 22×23, and 220×23, then you can also discuss how people used one problem to solve the next. In preparation for the next session, do some mental division, using $73 \div 4$ and $162 \div 15$.

Exit cards and homework

(5 minutes)

Distribute index cards and post the questions you want the group to reflect upon. As participants leave the seminar, distribute the Session 5 "Homework" sheet.

Video Summary

Building a System of Tens, Session 5

This 11-minute video segment presents third graders and fifth graders working on two multiplication problems.

29 × 4

First we see third-grade students working on the problem, "How many legs do 29 elephants have?" Two children, Ryshawn and Nicholas, present their solution methods to the class.

Ryshawn

Ryshawn thinks of the problem in terms of adding, that is, 4×29 is the same as $29 + 29 + 29 + 29$. He decomposes to make this easier.

$$25 + 25 + 25 + 25 = 100$$
$$4 + 4 + 4 + 4 = 16$$
$$100 + 16 = 116$$

Nicholas

Nicholas multiplies, but he breaks apart the problem.

$$20 \times 4 = 80$$
$$9 \times 4 = 36$$
$$80 + 36 = 116$$

The teacher, Nancy Horowitz, discusses her sense of Nicholas's work: that he has an awareness of being able to break numbers apart—that when he seemed stuck on this problem, she had only to ask him if he knew any multiplication facts that are close to 29×4, and he immediately thought of 20×4 and was on his way.

29×12

Jemea

Jemea, a fifth grader, explains to her small group how she solved the problem 29×12.

$$30 + 30 + 30 + 30 + 30 + 30 + 30 + 30 + 30 + 30 + 30 + 30 = 360$$
$$360 - 12 = 348$$

Working with Jemea's group, the teacher solicits an explanation of how they understand Jemea's idea. The teacher, Liz Sweeney, then summarizes what she saw happening in this small-group work.

This next sequence shows a group of fifth grade boys working on the problem 36 × 17.

Thomas B

> I did 36 bowls, and I put 17 cotton balls in each one.
>
> 10 × 17 = 170, and I just kept doing it, 170, 3 times. And then this one is different because it's 6 times.
>
> I took the 7s and the 10s apart and 10 × 6 was 60 and 7 × 6 = 42, and 42 + 60 = 102. Then I added those three 170s, plus the 102, and it came up to be 612.

Another boy asks where he got the 17, so Thomas B explains.

> The question was 36 × 17. Instead of going 17 × 36, I just used the 17s to put in here. There's 36 bowls, and I put 17 cotton balls in each one for 17 × 36.
>
> This is 17 × 10, this is another 17 × 10, this is another 17 × 10, this is 17 × 6.

Finally, a second child named Thomas presents an incorrect method for solving 36 × 17.

Thomas H

> I wanted to make 36 × 17 easier. So I added 4 to 36 to make it 40, and I added 3 to 17 to make it 20. So I timesed 40 × 20 to get 80 [*he says 80, but has written 800*].
>
> I knew it wasn't the answer, so I minused 4, because I added 4 to 36, and that brought me to 796 . . . and I minused 3 'cause I had to add 3 to get to 20, and I got the answer, 793.

The teacher, Liz Sweeney, acknowledges general uneasiness in the class over this last strategy, and asks the class, for homework, to think about how Thomas's strategy could be adapted to make it right.

Math Activity: Multidigit Multiplication

1. Write a word problem that would be solved by 16×18.

2. Create representations of 16×18 with diagrams, with base ten blocks, with Cuisenaire rods, and with Unifix cubes. Try to use each material in more than one way.

3. People frequently try to solve multiplication problems by applying procedures that work for addition. For each of the following examples, explain what is incorrect about the suggested procedure. How might the procedure be adapted to produce a correct answer?

    a. $16 + 18 = 14 + 20 = 34$. I took 2 from the 16 and gave it to the 18. Why not solve 16×18 by multiplying 14×20?

    b. $12 + 18 = (10 + 10) + (2 + 8)$. I added the tens, added the ones, and then added those totals together. Why not solve 12×18 by computing $(10 \times 10) + (2 \times 8)$?

    c. $36 + 17 = 40 + 20 - 4 - 3 = 53$. I rounded up to the nearest tens, added, and then compensated at the end by subtracting the extra 4 and 3. Why not solve 36×17 by computing $(40 \times 20) - 4 - 3$?

4. Consider your responses to question 3. What makes multiplication behave so differently from addition? What do you need to consider about multiplication as you modify strategies that are appropriate for addition to make them appropriate for multiplication?

Focus Questions

Chapter 5: Cases 18–21

Refer to the questions raised in the introductory text for these cases (page 71). Keep those questions and your reactions to them in mind as you discuss the following.

1. In Eleanor's case 18, Mark, Joel, Stephan, Jen, and Mika each offer strategies for computing 27×4. Try to compute 34×6 using each child's approach.

2. Later in case 18 (line 48), Eleanor reports about Jen working on 14×16. Discuss the method Jen uses. What were the elements of correct logic in her procedure? Where did her thinking go awry? Modify Jen's work so that her procedure produces the correct answer. Try another problem with this strategy. Will Jen's method work with all pairs of numbers?

3. Turn to case 20 (line 226) and consider Michael. How did he get 854 as the answer to 25×9? What were the elements of correct logic in his procedure? Where did his thinking go awry? Modify Michael's method so that his procedure is correct. Try another problem with this strategy. Will Michael's method work with all pairs of numbers?

4. In case 19, Lauren describes "cluster problems." Create a cluster of problems related to 37×26.

5. What have you learned or noticed about multiplication by working on these cases?

Homework

Portfolio assignment: Changes in your classroom

Unlike many in-service workshops, which present new teaching methods or new classroom activities, this seminar focuses on the central ideas that underlie elementary mathematics and on the thinking of students as they encounter those ideas. However, even though the seminar is not focused on teachers' *actions*, it may influence what happens in participants' classrooms.

Please write responses to these questions for the next session.

1. Have these sessions affected how you think about teaching? Have you noticed any shift in what you are thinking as you work with your students in math class?

2. Are there ideas from reading the cases or watching the video that you are planning to implement in your classroom. If so, what are they?

Reading assignment: Casebook chapter 6

Read chapter 6 in the casebook for *Building a System of Tens,* including the both the introductory text and cases 22–24. As you read, think about the questions raised in the chapter introduction.

Division with Multidigit Numbers

Preparation and Materials

■ **Background**

Read "Maxine's Journal," Session 6, pp. 151–157.

Read the agenda for Session 6.

■ **Case discussion**

Read the casebook, chapter 6.

Duplicate and review "Focus Questions" for chapter 6, p. 90.

Determine groups of three for small-group discussion (consider grade-level groups).

Obtain base ten blocks, interlocking cubes, and Cuisenaire rods.

■ **Viewing the video**

Obtain a video playback machine.

On the DMI Tape *Building a System of Tens*, locate and preview the Session 6 segment (16 minutes, 30 seconds).

Review the video summary, p. 86.

■ **Homework**

Duplicate "Homework" sheet for Session 6, p. 91.

Agenda

Discussion of group norms (25 minutes)

Now that the group has been working together for several sessions, it is a good idea to check in on issues relating to group norms. In particular, suggest that participants consider their role in the seminar when the mathematical topic under discussion is not explicitly part of their own curriculum. For instance, how did the upper-grade teachers participate in Session 3, "Written Numerals and the Structure of Tens and Ones," and how will the primary teachers make use of Session 6, "Division with Multidigit Numbers"? Ask people to think about their experiences in both whole-group and small-group discussions, and solicit comments about what makes the group work a positive learning experience for them.

Case discussion (60 minutes)

Small groups, 30 minutes

Whole group, 30 minutes

These cases present students' various ways of figuring out division problems. As with the multiplication explored in Session 5, teachers need the opportunity to work through this mathematics for themselves. You may want to group participants by grade level so that teachers of primary students do not feel at a disadvantage within the small groups because they do not teach this material.

Primary-grade teachers could reflect on the following question as they work: What part of the ideas of division and fair shares should your students encounter now so that they will be able to make sense of division when they are older?

Distribute "Focus Questions" for chapter 6 and ask small groups to work through the mathematics as they follow the students' methods for solving division problems. While the first three questions relate to specific children's strategies examined in the cases, the fourth question restates the general question that guided the reading of this set of cases: How is division similar to, and how is it different from, the other three operations? Announce the time schedule for these discussions: a half hour in small groups, and another half hour in the whole group. Remind them that the manipulatives are available.

Use the focus questions as a starting point for the whole-group discussion. Invite volunteers to explain their answers to questions 1, 2, and 3. Then turn the conversation to the more general question 4. If there isn't time to complete the discussion, reassure the group that they will have the opportunity to continue after viewing a video case of students working on these same ideas.

Break
(15 minutes)

Mental math
(15 minutes)

Announce that this mental math activity is related to the math in the video they will be watching next, with students working on division. First, ask participants to create a word problem that can be solved by calculating $159 \div 13$. Write two or three of these problems on the board. Next, ask them to perform $159 \div 13$ mentally and then share their strategies.

Viewing and discussing the video
(60 minutes)

The video segment for Session 6 presents several fifth graders explaining their approaches for computing $159 \div 13$. The segment runs about 17 minutes total, but announce that you will be showing the tape in sections, stopping periodically to discuss the children's strategies. After the children's approaches have been discussed, begin the whole-group discussion by asking, "What do these children understand that allows them to work this way with division?"

Exit cards and homework
(5 minutes)

Distribute index cards and post the questions you want the group to reflect upon. As participants leave the seminar, distribute the Session 6 "Homework" sheet.

Video Summary

Building a System of Tens, Session 6

This 17-minute video segment shows eight fifth-grade students who are explaining their ways of solving 159 ÷ 13. In this summary, the teacher's words are in italics; students' words are not necessarily exact quotes.

$$159 \div 13$$

Elaine

She goes to the board to explain.

> I did 13×10 because 10 is a landmark . . . and that's 130.

> Then I was 29 away from the right number, so I wanted to see how many 13s I could do. I knew 10 plus 10 is 20, and 13 only has 3 more than 10, so I added the 3s into it, and came up with 26.

> So I added 26 to 130 and got 156. So my answer was 156 remainder 3.

Your answer was 156 remainder 3?

> No, it would equal 12, because you're dividing.

Can someone rephrase what Elaine was saying?

Kyle restates Elaine's solution.

Yuriy

Yuriy also goes to the board to present his group's approach.

> First we thought $13 \times 13 = 169$. And it's 10 off, so we took 13 away, the closest we would have gotten counting by 13s, and we got $169 - 13 = 156$. And that was 3 less than 159, so we added 3: $156 + 3 = 159$.

> So our answer was twelve 13s and 3 left over, so it would be 12.3 [*he writes and says "twelve point three"*].

How did you decide to choose 13×13 to begin?

> It was like a number to round off.

Can you explain to me what you mean, "a number to round off"?

> You wouldn't just take some number like 13×15, like that would be in the middle or something. You might take a number that would be something you might know, so it would help you round off.

So you knew 13×13, and that felt like rounding off to you?

Yes.

So why did you take a 13 away?

> Because the 13 is what you were counting by, and you had to see what was the closest you could get with 13, and how much was left over.

Pointing to Yuriy's answer, 12.3, the teacher does not comment on the incorrect use of the decimal point, but verifies that the answer is 12 (thirteens) with a remainder of 3 (or 3 "left over").

Amelinda

Amelinda sets up the problem as if for long division, but then keeps subtracting 13 successively.

$$
\begin{array}{r}
13\overline{)159} \\
-13 \\
\hline
146 \\
-13 \\
\hline
133 \quad \textit{(and so forth)}
\end{array}
$$

> I put the 13 on the bottom, and I took away, and I kept taking away, and it left me with 12 remainder 3.

Where did you get 12?

> I kept taking away. I made a mistake, but I checked and fixed it, and I kept taking away. I counted how many 13s I took away. It was 12, and the remainder was 3 because I couldn't take away any more 13s.

Thomas

Thomas has drawn a chart showing 13 columns. He has written 10, 1, and 1 vertically in each column.

1	2	3	4	5	6	7	8	9	10	11	12	13
10	10	10	10	10	10	10	10	10	10	10	10	10
1	1	1	1	1	1	1	1	1	1	1	1	1
1	1	1	1	1	1	1	1	1	1	1	1	1

> What I did was, I had 159, I took 10 away, and as soon as I got to 10, I knew it was 100. I added them all together and got 130.

I minused 159 – 130. It brought me to 29. I gave each group 1 out of the 29, so I gave them 13.

I minused 13 from 29 and that gave me 16. So I gave every group 1 out of 16.

I minused 13 from 16 and it gave me 3. I counted how much I gave every group, and I gave every group 12 with 3 left over. So my answer was 12 remainder 3.

Shannon

I first broke it down into 59 and 100.

Why did you do that?

Because there was 59 in the tens and ones place and there was another 100, so we just figured it would be easier to work with two separate numbers.

In total, there were eleven 13s [4 in 59 and 7 in 100].

Shannon then added up the two remainders from dividing 100 by 13 [*remainder 9*] and 59 by 13 [*remainder 7, although she says 17 on the tape*] and got 16. There was one more 13 in the 16, with a remainder of 3, so she changed the eleven 13s to twelve 13s. Then she did 12 × 13 and got 156. She concludes as follows.

We couldn't get any closer with any more 13s, so we got the answer of 12 with a remainder of 3.

Alosha

I counted by 13s to 52. Then I kept adding 52s.

I'm going to stop you because you have something on your paper you're not including. [The teacher fills in 26 and 39 between the 13 and 52.] *Then you stopped at 52 and started adding those?*

52 + 52 is going to be pretty close.

Alosha adds them to get 104, then adds another 52 to get 156.

So with your 52s, how many 13s did you have there?

I counted the 13s to 52, which was 4, and just kept adding 4.

With the teacher's prompting, Alosha counts the 13s by fours.

Four 13s, eight 13s, twelve 13s. Then I knew that I was 3 off.

Call on someone to rephrase it for you.

Carla

She has drawn an array of 159 circles in rows of 10 and has drawn rings around groups of 13 circles.

> I drew 159 circles. I knew I had to make 13 groups. I circled 13. Then I counted how many groups I circled and it was 12. First I had remainder 4.

> Then I did 13 × 12. It was 156. So I knew the answer was 12 remainder 3.

Kevin

Kevin has used the traditional long division algorithm. Another boy describes Kevin's method, identified as "cross division," as "too complicated." At the teacher's request, Kevin then demonstrates his long division, getting 12 remainder 3. The teacher directs her next question to David, the other boy.

Why did you feel this was complicated?

> [*David replies*] I couldn't tell what he was thinking just by looking at it.

The teacher speaks to Kevin again.

Tell us how you are thinking when you do this strategy.

Kevin explains how he thinks through the first steps of long division. The teacher then breaks in to compare Kevin's strategy to David's strategy, not shown on this tape, but similar to Elaine's. She points out that both strategies look first at the number of tens in the answer: the first 1 that Kevin wrote in long division is the same as ten 13s.

$$
\begin{array}{r}
13 \\
\times\ 10 \\
\hline
130 \\
+\ 13 \\
\hline
143 \\
+\ 13 \\
\hline
156
\end{array}
$$

The teacher acknowledges that the traditional algorithm is complicated, but reaffirms its connection with many of the other strategies students have used.

BUILDING A SYSTEM OF TENS

Focus Questions

Chapter 6: Cases 22–24

Refer to the questions raised in the introductory text for these cases (page 87). Keep those questions and your reactions to them in mind as you discuss the following.

1. Consider the problem presented in Betty's case 22, represented as 72 pieces of candy shared among 3 people. Solve the problem by representing it with base ten blocks. Now solve the problem by using the familiar long-division algorithm. What similarities do you see between the two methods? What differences do you notice?

2. In Eleanor's case 23 (line 180), explain Jen's method of dividing 121 by 3. Try another problem using this strategy. Will it always work? Can you explain why?

3. In Janie's case 24 (line 259), April decides to divide up the 143 jelly beans among 8 people by seeing first how many 8s there are in 100 and then how many 8s there are in 43. She goes on to divide up the remaining 7 jelly beans. Try her method on another problem. Will it always work?

4. In what ways is division similar to each of other three operations? In what ways is it different? Where do you see the idea of "building a system of tens" arising in these cases?

5. Return to the introduction to chapter 6 and discuss the questions posed there.

Homework

Portfolio assignment: Reflecting on the cases

Go through chapters 1–7 in the casebook for *Building a System of Tens.* Pick one case that has had an impact on your thinking about mathematics, about learning, or about teaching. Describe that impact and your ideas. What made the case evocative for you?

Reading assignment: Casebook chapter 7

Read chapter 7 in the casebook for *Building a System of Tens,* including both the introductory text and cases 25–29. As you read, keep in mind the questions raised in the chapter introduction.

Decimal Numbers

Preparation and Materials

■ **Background**

Read "Maxine's Journal," Session 7, pp. 158–163.

Read the agenda for Session 7.

■ **Introducing the homework**

Duplicate "Homework" sheet for Session 7, p. 100.

■ **Math activity**

Duplicate "Math Activity: Working with Decimals," p. 98.

Obtain base ten blocks, graph paper, cubes.

Work through the activity yourself.

Determine working groups of three.

■ **Case discussion**

Read the casebook, chapter 7.

Duplicate and review "Focus Questions" for chapter 7, p. 99.

Determine pairs for small-group discussion.

■ **Exploring innovative curricular materials**

Choose and duplicate an activity from those suggested on p. 97 or from another curriculum your group wants to explore.

Agenda

Discussion of the portfolio assignment (15 minutes)

Start this session with a discussion of the Session 6 portfolio assignment. First provide 5 minutes for teachers to talk with a neighbor about the case they chose from the casebook that has had the greatest impact on them and why they chose it.

Open the whole-group conversation by asking participants to identify their chosen case. Then pose the more general question, What makes a case effective? You might alert participants that they will be writing a case of their own for the next class; through this discussion, then, they can start to think about how to write a case that stimulates discussion.

Introducing the homework (10 minutes)

Distribute the Session 7 "Homework" sheet and provide time for teachers to ask questions about the case-writing assignment. Announce that part of the next seminar meeting will be devoted to reading and discussing each other's cases in small groups. Emphasize that they should write about something of interest to them, and that this is an opportunity to pose questions about their own students' mathematical thinking. Point out that student dialogue and classroom details help the reader to understand how the students are thinking. Remind them to bring in *four copies* of their cases, for small-group reading and discussion.

Math activity (50 minutes)

Small groups, 30 minutes

Whole group, 20 minutes

In this math activity, "Working with Decimals," participants explore different ways that manipulatives can be used to represent decimal fractions. Gather the teachers into groups of three and distribute the math activity sheet. As you check in with the small groups, remind them to represent each number in at least two different ways. Following this initial work, you might pair up the groups of three and ask each group to explain their representations to the other. If you do this, begin the whole-group discussion by asking what complications were introduced by problem 2; then discuss the more general question, What issues about decimals did this activity highlight for you?

If you do not have the groups explain their representations to each other, then begin the whole-group discussion by asking groups to share their representations of .25 and .6 from problem 1. Then move on to representations for .007 and 1.3 from problem 2, asking what complications were brought up by this second set of numbers. Finally broaden the discussion to the question, What issues about decimals did this activity highlight for you?

Since the case discussion is likely to focus on some of the same issues, you might want to record participants' comments on easel paper for reference later in the session. It is likely that the group might want to continue this conversation past the time allotted. If so, assure them that the cases provide a different means to work through the same ideas and that they can pursue these same issues in that discussion.

Break

(15 minutes)

Small-group case discussion

(25 minutes)

In the cases in chapter 7, students are grappling with the meaning of decimal numbers, working at representing decimal numbers with concrete materials, and determining how to adjust their methods of calculating with whole numbers so the methods apply to numbers with decimals.

Ask teachers to return to their small groups. Distribute "Focus Questions" for chapter 7 and announce that teachers will have 25 minutes to work on these. The first two questions invite the teachers to analyze in some detail the mathematics involved in cases 25 and 28 (Henrietta's case and Nicole's March case). The third and fourth questions are more general, asking teachers to consider the ways our ideas about number must expand when we go beyond whole numbers to include decimal numbers. Advise the group that it is unlikely they will have time to fully discuss all of the questions; those not discussed by the group can be used individually for further thought.

Whole-group case discussion

(25 minutes)

Start the whole-group discussion by asking for responses to focus question 1. On easel paper, record participants' comments about Steven's reasoning in two columns: "What is logical in his thinking?" and "What is he missing?" Then turn the discussion to the more general questions: In what ways are Steven's confusions unique to decimals? How are they related to whole number place-value issues? Next, turn to focus question 2 and compile a list of the mathematical ideas participants have identified. Invite participants to use this list as they discuss question 3.

Exploring innovative curricular materials

(35 minutes)

Make available the curricular activity you have selected from the suggested list. Explain that participants now have an opportunity to investigate curricular materials that support student exploration of the mathematical ideas discussed in this seminar. Suggest that participants work in pairs and consider the following questions as they examine the selected student materials:

1. What mathematical ideas can be explored with this activity?

2. As you watch students engage in this activity, what kinds of questions might you ask them and why?

3. If you found this activity to be too difficult or too easy for a particular group of students, what modifications might you suggest?

Set aside the last 10 minutes for whole-group discussion of these same questions.

Exit cards and homework

(5 minutes)

Distribute index cards and post the questions you want the group to reflect upon at the close of this session.

Remind participants about their case-writing portfolio assignment that you introduced earlier in the session. Also call attention to the reading assignment, which poses a question about the essay "Highlights of Related Research" (chapter 8 of the casebook). Explain that rather than introducing new cases, this chapter presents views from the educational research community on the mathematical issues that were raised in cases 1–29.

Exploring Innovative Curricular Materials

Activities related to the math in Sessions 1–4

Choose one activity from this list for seminar participants to explore during Session 7.

Everyday Mathematics (Chicago: Everyday Learning Corporation)

"Place Value and Money Exchange Game." In *Second-Grade Everyday Mathematics by* M. Bell et al., 1998. See Lesson 6.

"Subtraction of Multidigit Numbers." In *Fourth-Grade Everyday Mathematics* by M. Bell et al., 1998. See Lesson 13.

Investigations in Number, Data, and Space (Palo Alto, CA: Dale Seymour Publications)

"Roll-a-Square." In *Putting Together and Taking Apart* by K. Economopoulos and S. Russell (grade 2, Addition and Subtraction), 1998. See Investigation 2, Session 2.

"Close to 1000." In *Money, Miles, and Large Numbers* by K. Economopoulos, J. Mokros, J. Akers, and S. Russell (grade 4, Addition and Subtraction), 1998. See Investigation 3, Session 1.

MathLand (Mountain View, CA: Creative Publications)

"Number Riddles" in "Along the Way." In *MathLand Grade 3 Guidebook* by L. Charles et al., 1995. See Unit 3, "Strategies," Week 2.

"Convince Me!" in "Along the Way." In *MathLand Grade 4 Guidebook* by L. Charles et al., 1995. See Unit 3, "Strategies," Week 3.

Math Trailblazers (Dubuque, IA: Kendall/Hunt)

"How Did They Do It?" in "Addition Seminar." In *Ways of Adding Larger Numbers* by P. Wagreich et al. (grade 2), 1997. See Unit 9, Lesson 2.

"The Fewest Pieces Rule" in "The TIMS Candy Company." In *Place-Value Concepts* by P. Wagreich et al. (grade 3), 1997. See Unit 4, Lesson 2.

Resources from Marilyn Burns (Sausalito, CA: Math Solutions Publications)

"Stars in One Minute." In *Math by All Means: Place Value* by M. Burns (grade 2), 1994.

"Is a Blue Whale the Biggest Thing There Is?" In *Math and Literature* by R. Bresser (grades 4–6), 1995.

Math Activity: Working with Decimals

1. Use graph paper, base ten blocks, cubes, or any other materials to represent decimal numbers. Find at least two ways to represent each of the following. At least one of your representations should be new to you.

   a. .25

   b. .6

2. How would you represent .007 and 1.3 with the systems you built in problem 1?

3. Use your representations to calculate .25 + .6, and then record both your process and your answer.

4. Use your system to represent .38, .45, and .38 + .45; record your process and your answer.

5. Use your representations to calculate .6 − .007; record both your process and your answer.

Focus Questions

Chapter 7: Cases 25–29

Refer to the questions raised in the introductory text for these cases (page 103). Keep those questions and your reactions to them in mind as you discuss the following.

1. In Henrietta's case 25 (line 6), Steven is working on the problem .25 + .6. He writes .211 as the answer, which he reads as "2 tenths and 11 hundredths." Explain the logic in what Steven is doing. Explain what Steven is missing.

2. The students in Nicole's case 28 are trying to determine which of two answers (2.06 or 1.529) is the correct answer to a decimal addition problem. Explain how they resolve this question. Make a list of the mathematical ideas you see in their work.

3. In what ways are the addition of whole numbers and the addition of decimal numbers the same? In what ways are they different?

4. Return to the introduction to chapter 7 and discuss the questions posed there.

Homework

Portfolio assignment: A case from your class

For the first seven sessions of this seminar, you have read cases written by teachers describing events in their own classrooms. In preparation for the next session, you will write a case based on your own class. This case should present the mathematical thinking of one or more of your students. To make the narrative understandable to your colleagues, include details such as dialogue and what you are thinking as you work with the students. To capture dialogue, some teachers find it helpful to tape-record a class session, in addition to taking notes during a discussion.

Your write-up should include your analysis of the mathematical thinking of the student(s) and the questions it raises for you. In our next session, we will meet in small groups to read and discuss one another's cases.

Reading assignment: Casebook chapter 8

Read chapter 8 of the casebook for *Building a System of Tens*, which takes another look at the mathematical issues in the cases through the essay "Highlights of Related Research." You might first reread the casebook "Introduction" (p. 1) for an overview of the broad themes explored in the cases.

As you read the research essay, think about this question: How does this article illuminate either the stories in the cases or the experiences you have had in your own classroom?

BUILDING A SYSTEM OF TENS

Highlights of Related Research

Preparation and Materials

■ **Background**

Read "Maxine's Journal," Session 8, pp. 164–170.

Read the agenda for Session 8.

■ **Sharing participants' cases**

Determine discussion groups of three.

■ **Discussion of the research essay**

Read the casebook, chapter 8, "Highlights of Related Research."

List the five themes from the essay on easel paper.

Determine two sets of groups for a "jigsaw" discussion; see p. 102.

■ **Exploring innovative curricular materials**

Choose and duplicate an activity from those suggested on p. 104 or from another curriculum your group wants to explore.

■ **Homework**

Duplicate "Homework" sheet for Session 8, p. 105.

Agenda

Sharing participants' cases   (60 minutes)

Small groups, 45 minutes

Whole group, 15 minutes

Gather teachers into groups of three. Suggest that they read all the cases written by colleagues in their group before they start any discussion. Then tell them to consider these questions: "What issues are common to the three episodes? What is unique to each one?" It will be up to each group to share the allotted 45 minutes equitably. After 30 minutes, announce that the whole-group discussion will begin in 15 minutes.

Start the whole-group discussion by asking the teachers to discuss the experience of doing this assignment and participating in discussions about cases they themselves had written.

Break   (15 minutes)

Discussion of the research essay   (65 minutes)

First small group, 20 minutes

Second small group, 25 minutes

Whole group, 20 minutes

Before beginning this work, explain the jigsaw procedure so that participants will understand their role in each of the small groups. In their first small group, participants will work to become familiar with one of the five sections of the essay. Then the groups will be shuffled. In the second small group, participants will be responsible for running that part of the discussion pertinent to the section they considered in their first group.

For the first 20 minutes, organize the participants into five groups and assign one section of the research essay to each group. In their small groups, participants should first clarify any questions they have about that section of the essay and then share ideas about how the theme relates to cases in the casebook or to events in their own classrooms.

After 20 minutes, reorganize the seminar into groups of five or six, making sure that each new group has at least one representative from each of the original small groups. Announce that groups will have a total of 25 minutes to

Building a System of Tens

discuss the essay, and suggest that they distribute the time evenly among the five original groups (i.e., 5 minutes per section).

You can begin the whole-group discussion by asking, "What was it like to read and discuss this essay?" This discussion can be an opportunity for participants to explore their ideas about the relevance of research. Many teachers consider educational research to be unconnected to their teaching experience. The author of the essay has made an effort to ground research results in examples from the cases in *Building a System of Tens,* allowing teachers to see more links between the classroom work they do and the work of the researcher.

Exploring innovative curricular materials (35 minutes)

This marks the second opportunity for teachers to examine curricular materials that allow their students to engage with the mathematical ideas of this seminar. Ask the participants to work in pairs, considering the following questions as they examine the selected student materials:

1. What mathematical ideas can be explored with this activity?

2. As you watch students doing this activity, what kinds of questions might you ask them, and why?

3. If you found this activity to be too difficult or too easy for a particular group of students, what modifications might you suggest to them?

Set aside the last 10 minutes for whole-group discussion.

Exit cards and homework (5 minutes)

Distribute index cards and post the questions you want the group to reflect upon.

Distribute the Session 8 "Homework" sheet. Point out the two parts to this assignment: collecting and analyzing student work, and reviewing their portfolio. Explain that they can bring in samples of work from any of their students; they need not return to the same three students whose work they selected for the first assignment for this seminar. These work samples will be discussed by the group in the first session of the next DMI seminar, *Making Meaning for Operation.*

Because the work samples offer a bridge between the two seminars, you may need to remind participants about this assignment shortly before the next meeting if the second seminar is not scheduled to begin soon after the end of *Building a System of Tens.* See page 20 for additional comments on this situation.

Exploring Innovative Curricular Materials

Activities related to the math in Sessions 5–7

Choose one activity from this list for seminar participants to explore during Session 8.

Everyday Mathematics (Chicago: Everyday Learning Corporation)

"Mammal Species: A Division Algorithm." In *Fourth-Grade Everyday Mathematics* by M. Bell et al., 1995. See Lesson 97.

"Whole-Number Multiplication Algorithms." In *Fifth-Grade Everyday Mathematics* by M. Bell et al., 1995. See Lesson 19.

Investigations in Number, Data, and Space (Palo Alto, CA: Dale Seymour Publications)

"Multiplication Clusters." In *Packages and Groups* by K. Economopoulos, S. Russell, and C. Tierney (grade 4, Multiplication and Division), 1998. See Investigation 2, Session 1.

"Smaller to Larger" (a decimal game). In *Name That Portion* by J. Akers, C. Tierney, C. Evans, and M. Murray (grade 5, Fractions, Percents, and Decimals), 1998. See Investigation 3, Sessions 3 and 4.

MathLand (Mountain View, CA: Creative Publications)

"Times Ten" in "Day Trip One." In *MathLand Grade 3 Guidebook* by L. Charles et al., 1995. See Unit 6, "Numbers Beyond and Between," Week 3.

"Digit Possibilities" in "Day Trip One." In *MathLand Grade 5 Guidebook* by L. Charles et al., 1995. See Unit 3, "Strategies," Week 4.

Math Trailblazers (Dubuque, IA: Kendall/Hunt)

"Planning Ahead," "Discuss," "Ordering Clay," and "Explore from Division." In *Connections to Division* by P. Wagreich et al. (grade 5), 1998. See Unit 9, Lesson 2.

Resources from Marilyn Burns (Sausalito, CA: Math Solutions Publications)

"How Long? How Many?" In *Math by All Means: Multiplication* by M. Burns (grade 3), 1994.

"The King's Chessboard." In *Math and Literature* by R. Bresser (grades 4–6), 1995.

Homework

Portfolio assignment: More children's work samples

1. Collect work samples from three students: one whose work you think is strong, the other two whose work is not so strong. Explain why the first sample satisfies you. What is your analysis of the other two? What are your learning goals for the three children?

2. As Part 1 of this DMI seminar comes to an end, it is appropriate to review your portfolio. Reread what you have written. Examine the items you have included. What changes in thinking do you see reflected in these assignments? In what ways has your thinking remained consistent? If you plan to continue with Part 2 of this seminar, *Making Meaning for Operations,* what questions will you be exploring?

Reading assignment: Casebook for Making Meaning for Operations

If you plan to continue with the second seminar, Number and Operations, Part 2, read the "Introduction" in the casebook for *Making Meaning for Operations.* Also read chapter 1, including the introductory text. As you read cases 1–7, consider the questions raised in the chapter introduction.

Maxine's Journal

Introductory note

"Maxine's Journal" was created to convey a sense of what a DMI seminar might look like—the type of discussions that can take place, the type of lessons seminar participants can draw from the sessions—and how it might feel to facilitate one.

Maxine is a composite character and so, too, are the teachers in her seminar. Though Maxine is fiction, her journal entries describe events and individuals observed and recorded by the developers of these materials and by those who piloted the first DMI seminars. Through the specificity of Maxine's references, the reader can gain many insights of a more general nature.

Because "Maxine's Journal" is based on early pilots of DMI, the specifics of a given session as Maxine describes it don't always coincide with the activities suggested in the agendas in this facilitator's guide. For example, only in later pilots did facilitators show us the importance of giving teachers the chance to analyze lessons from innovative curricula and using exit cards to get feedback at every session. Since these weren't part of the experience of Maxine's composite group, such activities are not addressed in "Maxine's Journal." Similarly, some cases included in the casebooks and on the video were later additions. However, despite these adjustments, the major themes addressed in DMI have remained consistent.

Maxine used the DMI Number and Operations seminars over a full year, meeting with her group for three hours approximately every other week. She presented Part 1, *Building a System of Tens,* in the autumn semester and Part 2, *Making Meaning for Operations,* in the spring. The portion of her journal included here covers the first seminar. Her journal for the second seminar is in the facilitator's guide for *Making Meaning for Operations.*

September 10

Goals for the seminar

Several months ago, a colleague challenged me to explain in 25 words or less what I think is important in teaching mathematics. I actually took on that challenge—thought about it for a few days—and this is what I came up with:

Children naturally have mathematical ideas. If they are encouraged to articulate them, they become aware of their own ideas and continue to have more. When classrooms are organized to encourage children to analyze their own, their classmates', and their teacher's ideas, then they will develop stronger and more refined concepts.

Well, that's 50 words—I couldn't even get it to 25. My colleague accepted this response.

Anyway, now that I am about to meet a new group of teachers for a seminar I haven't taught before, I'm thinking about what I want them to learn. What are my goals for this seminar?

First, I want the teachers to come to see that mathematics is about *thinking* and that *they* have mathematical thoughts. In my experience as a mathematics educator, I have learned that, for many teachers, their years as students in didactic-style mathematics classrooms have squelched their natural modes of mathematical thinking; they don't remember ever having had a mathematical idea. So one goal is to help teachers reconnect with their own powers of mathematical thought.

Second, I want the teachers to recognize their students as mathematical thinkers. I want them to learn to listen to their students' mathematical ideas and to respond in ways that communicate that those ideas are valued. I want their students to become aware of their own ideas and to continue having them.

Third, I want the teachers to learn how to analyze their students' ideas. What is the logic in what this child is saying? Even though there is something incorrect in the idea, why does it make sense to the child? How do these ideas relate to the central mathematical themes of the elementary curriculum?

Fourth, I want the teachers to learn how to engage a whole class in analysis of student ideas. How can the children learn to think about their classmates' ideas in relation to their own? How can the children learn to value sharing, refining, and revising their ideas through discussion with classmates? And how can this be done to help children learn the mathematics of the elementary curriculum?

Finally, whatever processes I envision for mathematics classrooms, I also envision for this group of adults. I want them to learn to pose their own questions about mathematics and come up with ways of thinking about answers. I want them to become curious about children's mathematical ideas and to learn how to listen carefully for those ideas. And I want them to think hard about what constitutes a teaching practice that supports children's development into powerful mathematical thinkers. This means having questions and ideas for themselves, sharing them, and also thinking hard about colleagues' questions and ideas. I call this "developing a stance of communal inquiry."

For the first seminar, we will be pursuing these goals while exploring the base ten structure of the number system. At the core of our investigations will be a body of classroom cases that allow us to examine how children put together ideas about place value and how they exploit the "base-ten-ness" of numbers when they invent their own computational procedures. I want the participants to see, on the one hand, that very complicated ideas underlie place value, and that what may seem obvious to them might not be obvious to children. On the other hand, they should also see that children approach mathematics with a great deal of inventiveness and that they can figure out how to compute with multidigit numbers without relying on the algorithms we all learned in school.

At the same time that they are investigating children's thinking, I hope that participants will be developing as mathematical thinkers. Throughout the *Building a System of Tens* seminar, they themselves will practice mental arithmetic, at first sharing their strategies for adding and subtracting multidigit numbers. From my past experiences with teachers, I assume that quite a few people will come to the seminar thinking that following the algorithms they teach is the only way to compute. And those who use their own, invented strategies are likely to feel a little ashamed, as though they are relying on "a crutch" or using "less sophisticated" methods. So, I'll need to begin by opening up those ideas. As they become more fluent in maneuvering about our number system, they will also need to be thinking about properties of the operations. In particular, they'll need to think through how the distributive property is implicated when multiplying or dividing multidigit numbers. Toward the end of the first seminar, the group will turn to representations of decimal fractions and consider how the ideas of place value they have been studying since the beginning of the seminar get played out to the right of the decimal point.

While teachers are investigating children's thinking as described in the cases, and while they are developing richer understandings of the number system, they will also be applying what they are learning to their own students' thinking. They will bring in samples of student work to share, conduct clinical interviews, and even write their own cases.

We'll conclude the seminar with a discussion about how the ideas we have considered are reflected in the research conducted in the last two decades. This will be an opportunity to think about the seminar as a whole and to integrate the ideas that we will have explored over eight sessions.

There's something paradoxical about my having a clear agenda for what I want the teachers to learn and, at the same time, believing so strongly that the seminar must be about the teachers' ideas. Perhaps the paradox is resolved when I think about my goals as helping teachers develop ways of thinking—ways of thinking about mathematics, about children's learning, and about teaching. This process involves recognizing one's own ideas and then refining or revising them. I also care that teachers be drawn to think about important issues. And, yes, I have a big role in selecting these issues and drawing their attention to them.

Still, in all of that, this seminar will be about teachers developing their own ideas. Maybe I'll need to watch this as the course progresses. To what extent am I respecting the ideas teachers bring and, at the same time, remaining true to my agenda for them?

The seminar will be meeting approximately once every two weeks for three hours, 4 to 7 P.M. I have the list of teachers who are signed up, but otherwise I know nothing about them—only that the names are unfamiliar. I don't know anything about their backgrounds in mathematics or the extent to which they are already oriented to my goals for the course. They have been sent packets of materials in order to prepare. For our first meeting, they have been asked to bring samples of the work of three students and to read the four cases in the first chapter of the casebook for *Building a System of Tens*. I'm nervous and excited.

**Session 1
Children's algorithms for adding and
subtracting two-digit numbers**

Maxine's Journal

September 11

Last night I had the first session with the new group. They are 18 teachers, none of whom has previously taken a course with me or my colleagues. Some are new teachers, most are veterans. They represent seven different school systems: urban, rural, and college town. They are all female.

We started the meeting with introductions and then engaged in three activities: sharing and discussing the student work they brought in, analyzing the first cases in the casebook, and playing the math game "Close to 100" and discussing what was learned from the game. We concluded the session by watching a short video clip.

Sharing children's work samples

For this first session, teachers had been given the following assignment:

> Collect work samples from three children. Choose one whose work you think is strong and two whose work is not so strong. Explain why the first sample satisfies you. What is your analysis of the other two? What are your learning goals for each of the three children?

In class, I asked them to get into groups of three to share what they had brought in. As I went from group to group, I noticed that teachers were showing and explaining their students' work, but no one was discussing it. They behaved more in a manner of taking turns than of true give-and-take, but this shouldn't come as a surprise. After all, these teachers may never before have taken a class where the focus was on *their* thinking, *their* observations, and *their* ideas, where the expectation was that *they* bring issues to the group and that *they* come to terms with the issues their colleagues raise.

It was interesting to me that, at different times during the 30 minutes of small-group discussion, four individuals found a way to come talk to me alone. Each wanted me to know that she was a traditional teacher, that she taught math by giving her students worksheets, and that she was nervous about being in this class. I think they all wanted me to know that they were fairly distant from the ideas presented in the cases; all they knew was the traditional algorithm—carrying and borrowing. I explained to each of them that I wasn't here to tell people to teach any differently. Rather, the seminar would provide an opportunity to think through some issues about mathematics and about children's learning. I want them to realize that this seminar is about *their* thinking, too, and not about something I'm trying to talk them into doing.

As I listened in on the teachers' reports (during the intervals between those anxious one-to-one conversations), it seemed clear that the homework questions had gotten them to think about some important things in a new way. Specifically, the question about learning goals for the three children, posed in the context of those students' work samples, made them consider that such goals could be formulated according to what they see in a piece of work. Apparently, some of the teachers had never thought of that before. That is, for them, learning goals were determined by the textbook and were the same for all children. To look at their students' work, try to figure out what they did or did not understand, and decide, based on that, what they needed to learn next—that was a new thought.

Mental math activity

In the first four cases the group read, three teachers (second grade and sixth grade) talk about their students' various strategies for adding and subtracting two-digit numbers. I started this part of the seminar by giving the teachers two problems to solve mentally: $57 + 24$ and $83 - 56$. Then we spent a few minutes talking about the different strategies they used. Some teachers worked with the numbers in ways that were quite similar to the methods presented in the cases; others said they pictured a piece of paper in their heads and performed the computation just the way they had been taught in school (just the way they were teaching it to their students).

Many of the teachers were giggling; they seemed nervous that their mathematics might not be as good or as sophisticated as someone else's. I was working hard to try to establish a nonjudgmental atmosphere. After each person spoke, I offered a comment to show that I took her contribution seriously. Since it was obvious that I was encouraging the group to think about alternative methods, this was particularly important for those who said they performed the computation using the algorithm they always taught and always used. I said that if they had a method that worked for them, it should be included for consideration by the group.

Case discussion: Discovering the child's perspective

After a ten-minute break, we turned to the cases. I had the teachers work in pairs on this task: Do the same problems we just solved mentally ($57 + 24$ and $83 - 56$), but this time try the methods used by the students in case 1 (Janae, Tom, Bert, and Betsy, for addition) and case 2 (Jason, Bert, Holly, and Joe, for subtraction). After they worked through the various methods, I had pairs join to form groups of four. I gave them the following questions to guide their small-group discussions.

1. What is the logic behind each student's procedure?

2. What is it that students need to understand about the numbers in order to do this?

3. What other issues come up for you?

I posed the first two questions because I wanted to focus the group on the mathematics and didn't want them to turn immediately to issues of classroom management or teacher behavior. I added the third to reassure the teachers that there would be time to address their particular concerns, too, if they wished—but only after they explored the mathematics.

People worked in small groups for 25 minutes before we met in whole-group discussion. The first thing the teachers said was that they had difficulty understanding some student solutions. In fact, it seemed that some folks were pretty overwhelmed. But as the discussion got rolling, several interesting points came up.

First, we spent some time on Joe's method for subtraction, since several groups had found his strategy to be the most challenging, and I had observed that people had found various ways to think about it. The group was able to say that, applied to 83 – 56, Joe's method went something like this:

$$80 - 50 = 30 \qquad 6 - 3 = 3 \qquad 30 - 3 = 27$$

There was some talk about whether Joe would say $3 - 6 = 3$ or $6 - 3 = 3$, but we finally agreed that *we* could say $6 - 3 = 3$. Now people needed to explain why it worked.

Patsy volunteered that she worked on it "algebraically." When I asked her to come to the easel to present her thinking, she wrote this:

$$
\begin{array}{ll}
83 & 80 + 3 \\
- 56 & 50 + 6 \\
\hline
& (80 - 50) + (3 - 6) \\
& 30 + -3 \\
& 27
\end{array}
$$

Although everyone could follow Patsy's steps, her method seemed no more obvious than Joe's, so I asked others to explain what they had done to convince themselves of its validity.

Claire said that it helped her to think about money. "Like, let's say I have 83 cents, 8 dimes and 3 pennies, and I want to buy something for 56 cents. After I put down 5 dimes, leaving me with 3, I still need to pay 3 cents more than my number of pennies." Marjorie, who was in Claire's group, said it was hard for her to follow what Claire was saying, so she drew a picture of it for herself. Then Marjorie came to the easel to show us:

OOOOOOOO XXX
OOOOO   XXXXXX

"The circles stand for dimes," she said, "and the X's stand for pennies. You can see that you cross out five circles, leaving three. Then you can cross out three X's, but you still have three more that you have to take away. So, three dimes is 30 cents, take away three cents, is 27."

Patsy added, "It's not clear exactly what Joe was thinking. What if he had 47 – 32? How would he do that? 40 – 30 = 10, 7 – 2 = 5? Now would he still subtract the 5 from the 10, or add it?"

I asked what the group thought. Nadia was quick to point out the rule that works: If the larger number in the ones place is on top, then you add; if it's on the bottom, then you subtract. To which Patsy responded, "But does Joe know that?"

At this point I started to get the sense that a few teachers were able to think clearly about Joe's method and about the other children's strategies as well, but many participants seemed overwhelmed. The very existence of addition and subtraction strategies other than the ones they had learned in school and taught for years was a new idea. And the notion that children invent such strategies was completely foreign.

When I suggested that some members of the group might be finding it hard to follow all the different strategies, several teachers made assenting sounds. Marta spoke up and said that she thought the students' methods were very confusing. Helen responded, "Look, they might be confusing to us as we try to follow them, but I bet they were not confusing to the kids who used them. It's probably clearer to that individual kid than what we think might be easier." Then Velma pointed out that we were trying to make sense of a bunch of different methods, and that's what makes it overwhelming, but each kid probably had only one of these clear in his or her head.

Later in the discussion, more people started thinking about the child's perspective. As we talked about different ways to solve 28 + 39, Helen mentioned that, in doing the traditional algorithm, we say "8 + 9 is 17; put down the 7 and carry the 1." But when kids do that and write 7 first and then 1, it seems like writing 71. So now she had this idea that, instead, we could say that they should write the 17 on the first line, and then, adding 20 + 30, write 50 on the second line. Then it's easy to add:

$$
\begin{array}{r}
28 \\
+\ 39 \\
\hline
17 \\
+\ 50 \\
\hline
67
\end{array}
$$

Most of the teachers got really excited, seeing this as a method of recording they could introduce to students to help them make fewer errors. They played around with this device a bit more, even for subtraction, and began to feel that it was much clearer than the way they have been teaching.

At this point, I became concerned that they now imagined this procedure would solve all their students' problems. So I raised that as a question, asking if they thought that if the textbooks would simply present *this* algorithm, everyone was going to be OK. I wasn't sure if they got the point of my question; it certainly didn't go anywhere. But I was glad I asked it. I think it alerted them to the fact that, in thinking about two-digit computation, there is more at issue than a method of recording one's steps.

When I said that, I didn't want to take from them their feeling that this procedure more nearly matches what one really does than the traditional method. Though Marjorie did say, "You know, we are all drawn to this, but who is to say this matches the kid's thinking? It might not."

At another point in the discussion, as we were breaking up numbers and putting them together again, Claire observed, "Look, it's not only knowing that you can break up numbers any way you choose, it's also a matter of knowing when it's convenient to break them up by tens."

I thought this was a really important contribution, but after that, the discussion slowed down. There weren't a lot of new ideas, and I was thinking that I needed to come up with another question, but I wasn't sure where we should go next. And then I thought, maybe this discussion has wound down and I should just end it. But before I could say anything, Nadia, sitting next to me, said very quietly, "You know, this makes me really wonder about our responsibility for teaching them 'the way to do it.' I mean, don't they really need to know the standard algorithm in order to do well on their tests? But if they can really do the problem, does anyone really know what it is they are doing? I'm very confused about it."

And this started an interesting conversation about what an algorithm really is. Actually, that's the way I paraphrased the issue for them, because they didn't have a word to use for a solution procedure. In fact, I've found that the word *algorithm* is frequently used incorrectly. I wanted to introduce the term and define it so that all the people in the group would mean the same thing by it. I told them that an algorithm is not a number problem or a math fact. It's a rule—a set of steps—for solving a particular kind of problem. An algorithm for calculating can be performed on any numbers. For example, we could define Joe's algorithm for subtracting two-digit numbers: Subtract the tens. Find the difference between the ones. If the larger number in the ones place is on top, then add the difference to the tens; if it's on the bottom, subtract the difference from the tens.

With *algorithm* defined for everyone, we returned to Nadia's concern. Some folks said that using different strategies is really doing mental math, but to work with pencil and paper, the kids have to know the other way. There wasn't much conversation about linking standard algorithms to what the children do on their own. Standard algorithms and children's methods were talked about as if they were very different things.

Thinking back on that long silence that ended up spawning such an interesting question, I recognize something I've been through before. When there is a long, uncomfortable silence, is it my responsibility to fill it? At the moment, I usually feel, "This discussion is falling flat, and I should be doing something about it." But almost always, if I wait it out, an important idea emerges from the quiet. Maybe, if I'd filled up that silence myself, we wouldn't have had that discussion—or at least, not then.

Math activity: Close to 100

"Close to 100" is a game that comes out of *Investigations in Number, Data, and Space,* the K–5 curriculum from TERC, published by Dale Seymour (1998). Players work with a set of number cards, each card bearing a single digit, 0 to 9. A player draws six cards and selects four of them to form two 2-digit numbers, summing as close to 100 as possible.

The teachers spent about 25 minutes playing the game in pairs. They seemed to be quite engaged, working hard to figure out which sets of numbers would get them close to 100 and thinking about the strategies they were using to find them.

When I sat down with one group, Tammy had asked how to adapt the game for use with second graders, and Claire was responding, "What is it you want your second graders to learn?" Tammy paused and then said, "Yes, this is what I have trouble with. There are lots of interesting activities that I know are good, but I don't have a purpose—or the purpose isn't clear to me. Either I don't know the math, or I just don't see what the kids should be getting." She said she was going to go back and think about how she might use this game with her students, and also think about what her point would be. I was quiet throughout this exchange, but I felt good that some of the teachers were pondering what they wanted their students to learn, instead of simply identifying activities to give them. I expect that, throughout the course, I'll be looking for opportunities to highlight that distinction. I want the teachers to learn how to set a *mathematical* agenda for their students, rather than simply take their students through a series of mathematical activities.

When we got together to talk about the different strategies they used, several interesting issues arose. Nadia said that, initially, she was so focused on finding numbers that add up to 10, she kept getting 110. That is, she put together numbers to make up a 10 in the ones place and then a 10 in the tens place, giving her 11 tens! It took her several rounds to realize that her strategy wasn't helping her get to 100.

Later in the discussion, Joan said that at first she picked the two highest digits to make one of her two-digit numbers as large as possible, and then worked with the other digits to get close to 100. But then she saw that she would be better off working first with the two digits that would go in the tens column.

Carla admitted that she started out concentrating on the ones, thinking about whether she had to carry or not. She said it took time to realize that, in this task, the tens are of primary importance; the ones, secondary.

Toward the end of this discussion, Marjorie asked if anyone had tried to make two 50s. When no one said they had, Marjorie commented, "Isn't that what we are really wanting?"

Since time was almost up (it was now 6:50 P.M.), that was how the question was left. But, more interesting to me than the mathematical question she posed was the tone of her question. At this point, folks had really started listening to, and building on, one another's ideas.

Viewing the video

I said to the group that we had done a lot of hard thinking today and that I expected we would continue to think hard like this for the rest of the course. But before this session ended, I wanted to leave them with some visual images. We would look at a video clip in which children explain their solution methods for adding two-digit numbers.

One thing we get from video is seeing teachers and students of various races and linguistic groups. The print cases, too, are based on the work of children and teachers from various backgrounds and in urban, rural, and suburban settings; but in the casebook, such identifiers are invisible. The video brings the cases to life.

I turned on the video, and we watched three children working on $48 + 25 = 73$. At the end of the segment, there was a long pause before Marta spoke up, "Those are real kids!" Once she broke the ice, a few more people made comments that conveyed the same message. It seems that, although we had been reading about the different strategies children developed for adding and subtracting, it had been difficult for the teachers to picture real children saying these things. But here they were, looking and sounding like children we have all known. I imagine that having seen this video will change the teachers' experience of reading the cases.

Maxine's Journal

September 25

At the beginning of any course—at least one that relies heavily on the participants' ideas—it is critical to figure out where people are starting from. Throughout this second session, I was brought up short by how "off" my expectations were. I don't know if the issues I'm facing would be typical of any group new to the ideas underlying this seminar, or if I'm dealing with things particular to this set of teachers.

The agenda for this session went like this: In the first part of the session, we worked from a video in which children present their strategies for solving two-digit subtraction computations. We then turned to the cases in chapter 2, which introduced some new ideas. I wanted folks to spend a generous amount of time in their small groups, working through the children's mathematics. When I called a break, some people continued working right on through it. Then the whole group met to discuss the cases. At the end of the case discussion, we devoted some time to reflecting on what our first two sessions had been like. I asked the group to think about what makes a discussion work well and to come up with a list of norms to keep in mind as we proceed.

Discussing cases from the video

We spent the first 5 minutes of class time going over participants' names; then we began to work from the video. It was, to some extent, a review of the mathematical content we had worked on last session: following the logic of children's invented algorithms for subtraction of two-digit numbers. However, the video added some new dimensions. First, as I mentioned in my reflections last time, there's something critical about getting images of classroom scenes, *seeing* the children doing and saying the things the teachers have been reading about. These aren't just children so special the teachers can't possibly imagine them. No, these children look and act like the students they know—there are long pauses in the children's speech; they fidget; and some speak so softly it's hard to hear. Second, with the video, the teachers get a chance to follow student thinking in real time. With the written cases, teachers can dwell on a student's words, read them over and over, and take time to think through the logic. This is a luxury they won't have in their own classrooms. Watching the video, teachers get to practice following student thinking in the time it takes the child to speak. And finally, there are some new strategies presented in the video that the group didn't work on in Session 1.

I introduced the video by reminding the group of something Claire had said in our last class: "It's not only knowing that you can break up numbers any way you choose, it's also a matter of knowing when [and why] it's convenient to break them up by tens." I told them that we'd be watching children who have different methods for solving subtraction problems, stopping after every child to become clear about the steps in the method of solution. I asked the teachers to take notes on each child so they'd be able to keep track in our discussions.

The first three children on the video present their methods for solving 40 − 26. Like many of the children we had seen in the print cases, Lisa's strategy involves decomposing 26 into 20 and 6. Unlike the others, however—and the teachers commented on this—Lisa subtracts the ones first, and then the tens.

When given other numbers to try out Lisa's method, like 54 − 38, the teachers said that Lisa would have subtracted 8 and then 30, but they weren't sure how she would treat the 54. Patsy thought Lisa would do it this way:

$$54 - 8 = 46$$
$$46 - 30 = 16$$

But Claire thought she might first break up the 54:

$$50 - 8 = 42$$
$$42 - 30 = 12$$
$$12 + 4 = 16$$

In fact, we don't know what Lisa would have done. But I was pleased that the teachers are considering these different possibilities.

James's method created a bit of a stir. Like Lisa, he decomposes 26 into 20 and 6, but he also breaks 40 into 20 and 20. He then subtracts 20 − 20 and 20 − 6, and ends up with 14. Marjorie asked if we could look at that clip again, which several people seconded, so I rewound the tape and we watched James explain his solution.

"So he divided 40 in half," Nadia said. "He got the right answer, but why would he do that?" I suggested that we look at another pair of numbers, 50 − 26, to see if everyone agreed.

Nadia said, "OK. So 50 is 25 and 25, and 26 is 20 and 6. Then 25 − 20 = 5 and 25 − 6 = 19. Add 19 and 5 and you get 24. But that seems so complicated! Besides, would he add or subtract the 19 and 5?"

Claire said she was thinking about it a different way. "What if he wasn't splitting 50 in half? I think he'd make it 20 and 30, choosing the numbers to match the 20 in 26. Then he'd have 20 − 20 = 0 and 30 − 6 = 24."

"Oh, yeah," Nadia agreed. "That makes more sense."

The group was fascinated by the third child, Naillil, who adds: 26 + 4 = 30, 30 + 10 = 40, and 4 + 10 = 14, so the answer is 14. Marjorie said, "When I was watching, I was completely confused about what she was doing and how she knew to add 4 + 10. But then the teacher asked her to explain. The girl said she had 26 marbles and wanted to have 40, so she needed to figure out how much to add to 26 to get 40. She added 4 marbles first, and then she added 10 more. That's so neat!"

The next two children work on 35 – 16. The teachers were surprised to see the first child, Glen, use "Joe's method"! At least, that's what Nadia called it. In Session 1, we had talked a lot about Joe's method, and here Glen was doing the same thing:

$$35$$
$$\underline{-\,16}$$
$$20 - 1 = 19$$

Glen subtracted 10 from 30 to get 20 and 6 from 5 to get –1, resulting in 19.

The teachers were surprised not only to come across that method again, but also to hear a second grader talk about "negative 1." I reminded them that in Emily's case in the casebook [case 4, "Learning Math While Teaching"], another second grader was reported to have done the same thing.

The last child on the tape, Becky, sets up the problem 35 – 16 vertically and solves it incorrectly, "5 – 6 = 0 and 3 – 1 = 2."

$$35$$
$$\underline{-\,16}$$
$$20$$

I thought we would spend a few minutes talking about Becky's logic, but Sheila instead blurted out, "I don't see why those teachers are teaching so many different ways to subtract. Why don't they just do one way, and then they can all do it?" This was the first indication of the evening that my sense of the group was way off. At the time, I was shocked; I wasn't sure I had heard her right, and so I asked Sheila to repeat her question. Did she really think the teachers had taught the children all those different procedures? I looked around the room, but nobody was protesting.

Now that I step back, I realize that I shouldn't have been shocked at all. As I wrote in my pre-seminar entry, I already know that many teachers lose touch over the years with their ability to generate mathematical ideas; they also tend to forget, or never realize, that children naturally have their own ways of thinking about numbers and calculation. And so, as they work from the cases, of course they'll interpret what they read and see in those terms—to them, obviously, the teacher or some other adult must have demonstrated all these different methods for the children to imitate.

At that moment, I didn't know what to do. On the basis of our discussions at our last meeting and the comments made about the five children in the video, I had assumed the group realized that most of the methods the children presented were their own invention, including Becky's incorrect one. So I said, "Sheila has posed a question we can think about and return to. What do the children learn from working with the different methods? What do they learn if they are all taught to do it the same way? If we turn to the print cases, we might have some more ideas about this."

I thought about whether I should have brought the group back to Becky's method. Perhaps analyzing what was missing for her would have helped. But I was uneasy with the tension in the room and decided to move on.

Small-group case discussion

Although my response to Sheila might not have been the most gracious segue into the next activity, I was stating what I hoped we would work on. The cases in chapter 1 and in the video clips we had seen involved children's invented strategies for adding and subtracting. To devise such strategies, the children must already have understood the composition of numbers in terms of tens and ones—or hundreds, tens, and ones. The cases in chapter 2 highlight children who are in the process of putting these ideas together, and I wanted the teachers to examine this process.

In four of the cases, the children are using manipulatives—base ten blocks, Unifix cubes, and Cuisenaire rods. (These are the first cases involving manipulatives.) Only a few minutes into small-group discussion, I realized that many of the teachers in our group had never seen these materials and would require time to become familiar with them before they could begin to follow what the children were doing. Though I had brought sets of the materials with me into our room—and here was another surprise—no one left her seat to get some. I had just assumed that they would recognize their need to handle the materials and would know to get them for themselves. Instead, I had to suggest they do so.

At this point, deciding I had better offer more structure and guidance for their small-group discussions, I wrote the following on the board:

> *Janine's student, Serena, used base ten blocks.*
> *Lucy's student, Sarah, used Unifix cubes.*
> *Emily's student, Julie, used Cuisenaire rods.*
>
> *1. Take a set of each type of manipulative and figure out how it can be used to represent number. Demonstrate how the different manipulatives can model 35 + 26 = 61 and 72 − 34 = 38.*
>
> *2. When we come together as a group, we will go over what you found for question 1 first. Then we will look closely at Janine's and Lucy's cases. What was Serena confused about, and what did she learn? What was Sarah confused about, and what did she learn?*

I wrote question 1 to ensure that those teachers who needed to were going to figure out for themselves what the manipulatives were and how they could be used. I added question 2 to communicate that we would still have our discussion of student thinking.

Once I changed my instructions, the teachers sat down with sets of manipulatives to figure out how to use them. I stood back for a few minutes to let groups get into their conversations and then approached Tony, Amira, and Shannon—all of whom, it seems, had never used anything like this before. Holding up a cube in one hand, Amira said, "I can see that you can count with these." Then, raising a base ten rod in her other hand, she added, "But I don't get what this is." When she noticed me listening, Amira froze. Clearly, she didn't want to say anything in front of me. Shannon stepped in to save her; she turned to me and, indicating a base ten rod, asked, "What are these?"

I smiled and said, "It's not at all obvious, is it? I've seen other groups of teachers quite puzzled by them. But I'll tell you one interesting story a second-grade teacher told me. She said that each year, some time in October, she'd bring out a set of those blocks and let her students play with them. After they got used to them, she posed the question, 'How might these be used for the math we've been doing?' This particular year, the class got into a debate about it. They all agreed that these small cubes would each stand for 1. But while most of the students thought the rod should stand for 10, one boy said that he thought it should be 42. So, let's think about that. Why would some children say it's 10 and one child say it's 42?"

Amira still seemed embarrassed, but Tony and Shannon were willing to think about it. Tony suggested, "This rod is like 10 cubes attached, but I don't get the 42."

"Right," I said. "How could anyone look at this and see 42?"

Then Shannon smiled. "I see it. You've got 10 squares on this side," she said, drawing her finger down the length of one side of the rod, "and 10 on this side, and this side, and this side. And one on each end. That's 42!"

I responded, "Yeah, I think that's probably what that child was thinking. According to the teacher, in the end he said it could be seen both ways, but for math class, he agreed, it's more useful to think of it as 10." I then left the group to let them explore the other manipulatives and practice adding and subtracting with them.

Even as I encouraged groups like Amira, Tony, and Shannon's to begin thinking about manipulatives, when I listened to the teachers who were already familiar with them, I was concerned that everything seemed so simple: The Cuisenaire rods aren't very good because they aren't scored; the Unifix cubes could be useful if the children are accustomed to keeping them in sticks of ten; and once students learned how to use the base ten blocks, they would understand the mathematics. The observations they made about the differences among the materials are valid—and important. My concern was with their confidence that base ten blocks provide *the* key to unlocking the number system. The process of coming to understand the system of tens is more complicated than that!

But here I need to pause and examine my own reactions. I should have understood that if a teacher believes it is his or her responsibility to make things clear to students and to keep them from becoming confused, the drive to find clear-cut and simple solutions will be strong. My own expectation that the teachers will examine the complexity of the mathematical ideas runs counter to that drive. It is simply too painful to wrestle with that complexity if they can't immediately see how to rescue their students from confusion. So what is my agenda? What do I want the teachers to learn? I guess one thing I want them to appreciate is that avoiding confusion is not a useful goal. Can they come to see that confusion is a necessary part of the learning process? that a person who has come up against a point of confusion now has an opportunity to learn?

But that is not my immediate goal for Amira, Tony, and Shannon. Instead, for Amira it is simply that she become comfortable enough in this class to be able to think! And for Tony and Shannon, my goal is that they begin to expand their ways of thinking about mathematics.

Once groups turned to the cases, I tried to help them look more closely at what the students were doing and saying. Could they articulate what was going on with Serena? Then I wanted them to follow more carefully just what happened with Sarah. Did something productive come out of the Unifix cube representation that Sarah made up for herself? I kept these questions in mind as we moved into whole-group discussion.

Whole-group case discussion

The teachers felt satisfied that their small groups had sufficiently addressed question 1—finding ways to represent 35 + 26 = 61 and 72 – 34 = 38 with the various manipulatives—and so we turned directly to the cases.

When I called the group's attention to Serena, in Janine's case "Thinking About Tens" [case 5], Patsy spoke up first. She said that Serena clearly had one-to-one correspondence but needed to be taught how to use the base ten blocks. I asked if anyone had a question about what's meant by "one-to-one correspondence," and there was a murmur that, no, they were clear about that. So I asked, "What did Serena learn?" Claire suggested that at first Serena's method of adding was to make tally marks to represent each of her numbers and then count them up. Since that was very slow and cumbersome, the teacher wanted Serena to learn to use base ten blocks.

I was concerned about this idea that "learning the manipulative" was all that Serena needed to do. Did they see that there was a mathematical idea in there? So now I asked, "What was hard for Serena in learning to use the base ten blocks?" After a long silence, I suggested that people look back at the case, starting around line 49. What's going on with Serena there?

Marjorie suggested that Serena needed to develop confidence that the 10-stick was really the same as 10 units. Velma said that she needed to see that the number in the tens place was the number of sticks and the number in the ones place was the number of cubes. Reflecting on this discussion now, I wish I had asked folks to talk about Kara's case, "Counting Money" [case 10]. That would have given them a chance to think about another child who preferred to use tally marks.

But at the time, I decided this was enough. There will be other cases that will allow the group to examine the idea here—a difficult idea for many children—which goes beyond learning to use the base ten blocks. We'll see if they get to recognize what a big cognitive step it is for a child to be able to count ones and also groups of 10 ones, keeping both results simultaneously in mind. Almost all the children in chapter 1, and the children in the video, have this down.

As I look back over Janine's case, I can see why the teachers might read it as an example of learning to use the base ten blocks. After all, Janine herself is pretty focused on the manipulatives. Actually, if teachers who are seeing these manipulatives for the first time have learned how the base ten blocks can be used to represent numbers and model calculations, I suppose that's plenty for now.

But when we turned to Lucy's case, "Keeping It Straight" [case 6], I was again struck by the group's need to find a simple fix; several people talked about what they would have done with Sarah to prevent her from making mistakes. Mainly, they said that Sarah needed to have a larger block for the quantity 10; she shouldn't have represented tens with a different color block the same size as a one. Despite my questions to the small groups, few teachers noticed that, in the course of the episode, Sarah had corrected herself. They skipped over this evidence and did not ask if she was developing a deeper understanding of multidigit addition.

So at this point, I stopped the discussion and had someone in the group act out how Sarah had come up with 174 when combining 45 and 39. Once everyone agreed with the demonstration, we turned back to the text to read together what happened next; I actually asked someone to read it aloud. Then my next question was, "How did Sarah change her model to come up with 84, the answer she already knew was correct? What did she understand to begin with, and what did she figure out in her interaction with Lucy?"

Marta was looking back at the first page of the case and shared what the teacher had written about Sarah: "She understood all the various methods that had been presented." And a little further on, "She had demonstrated in earlier lessons that she was already able to use the conventional algorithm." I appreciated that she was using the text this way, looking for the evidence the author has given us about what Sarah understands.

Now Patsy held up the cubes. "See," she said. "When Sarah made up her new method, she counted black cubes as ones and yellow as tens. When she added 45 and 39, she put the cubes together and had too many in the ones place. So she broke off ten from the ones and attached them to the tens. Then she counted the 10 ones as 10 tens. That was her mistake."

I asked if someone would paraphrase what Patsy had said. (I frequently use this as a strategy when I think ideas are moving too quickly, and I want to slow things down so that others can figure out what is being said.) There was a pause. I think the request to paraphrase was confusing to them. But then Velma complied, and Patsy affirmed that it was an accurate paraphrase.

I said that I thought it was important to be able to sort out what Sarah was doing and where her error came from, and asked for another paraphrase, which Helen offered.

I was still concerned about people wanting to set things up so that Sarah would have avoided the mistake in the first place. But instead of sticking with the case, I asked the group to think about the work they did with "Close to 100" in the previous session. What were some of their early strategies that didn't work? What happened when they discovered that they didn't work? After a few minutes of discussion, I asked what it would have been like if I had set things up to prevent them from formulating and testing out those initial strategies.

There was a long pause, and I was beginning to fear that my question felt like a put-down. But maybe the teachers were just taking time to think back. Finally, Nadia spoke up: "Right. You know, at first I kept getting 110, and then I saw what I was doing wrong. What would it have been like if you had said, 'Make the ones digits add up to 10 and the tens digits add up to 9'? The point was that I saw I was doing something wrong and I figured out how to fix it."

Once Nadia made that observation, perhaps I should have gone back to the question about Sarah—to help the group make the connection. But the conversation had already been long and difficult, so we ended it there.

Establishing norms for group discussion

By now we were approaching the end of our second session and had behind us five and a half hours of working together. For many people, the structure of our sessions and my expectations about participation were completely new. It was a good time to check in and make some of these expectations explicit. It was also time to establish some guidelines for ensuring that our discussions felt productive and open to everyone.

I was thinking that I had been working extremely hard at facilitating the discussions—especially when we were working on the cases. Even so, there were quite a few teachers who had never spoken up. Why weren't they talking? What were they thinking?

I started out by mentioning that these first two sessions were typical of the work we would be doing together in the seminar. That is, most of the time would be spent in group discussion—sometimes in pairs or small groups, sometimes in large group—and, in most sessions, part of the time would be spent working on the cases and some of the time would be spent on the mathematics itself. On occasion, they would also be talking about their own work with children. I said that at this point I wanted to hear how they were feeling and that I wanted us all to think about how to make group participation more comfortable for everyone.

It took some time to get the discussion moving, but eventually we arrived at the idea that, as people work in groups, they have different kinds of responsibilities: those to themselves and those to the group. We ended up soliciting responses to two questions: What do you do for yourself as a learner? What do you do to function as a group member? The thing is, once we started to generate the list, items didn't fall neatly into one category or the other; they applied to both. This is the list we came up with:

Ask questions.

Indicate that you've heard someone else's idea.

It's all right to disagree.

Would like a respectful response.

Sometimes we're not respectful and get a little angry. We need to move beyond the anger.

Sometimes it's useful to establish ground rules beforehand.

Don't take things personally.

When we do disagree, it's important to clarify what we think the other person has said.

Sometimes you think you heard something that wasn't said.

Sometimes I need to get my own thoughts together before I start listening to what someone else is saying.

Notice when you're overwhelming others through your own excitement.

Sometimes it feels like you're adrift in a rowboat with people who have speedboats.

If necessary, say, "I'm not following you."

We also listed ground rules for the seminar:

Start and end on time. (This applies to the whole seminar session and to the parts of a session.)

For the first few meetings, review names. Do something to reconnect.

Everyone should come prepared.

Monitor yourself.

Participate as an active listener.

Toward the end, Patsy said that everyone should contribute to discussions. But when Marjorie asked, "How can you set things up so that everyone can talk?" Marta objected, "Is it really important that everyone talk? What if it works better for some people to listen and not talk as much? Can we accept that some people might choose to be quiet?"

It was now 7 P.M., and so we ended there. But that last question is something I need to think about. In any group, there are lots of personalities—some people find it easy to talk and some find it difficult. Why do I want quiet people to speak up? Sometimes, I know, quiet people have good ideas that will enrich the group. And sometimes, I know, quiet people want to speak, and will learn more by having their ideas out there, but they need encouragement. Still, that's not always the case. In past classes, some teachers have assured me that they're learning a lot and that it's better for them not to feel pressured to speak up in the whole group. The thing is, when people are quiet, I have to initiate other mechanisms to find out what's going on with them.

Further reflections

As I look back over the session, I now think we should have spent a few minutes at the end doing some mental arithmetic. The discussion about norms had slowed, and returning to math would have raised the energy level. The next time I teach this seminar, I think I should introduce some three-digit computations to increase the complexity of the exercise and let them see that they can meet the challenge.

Session 3
Written numerals and the
structure of tens and ones

Maxine's Journal

October 9

The issue highlighted for me in this week's session is the difficulty teachers have with the shift of focus from their own teaching behaviors to their students' thinking. Methods courses, teachers' evaluations, professional discussions, and curriculum decisions are traditionally all about what the teacher should *do.* The idea that what a teacher does should be grounded in an understanding of *how students learn* and of *what they should learn* seems obvious only in retrospect. To most of the teachers in my group, this is not yet apparent. And because they have not yet developed the habit of attending to students' mathematical thinking, I find that, in facilitating case discussions, I'm struggling to move their attention away from the *teachers* in order to get to the *students:* What do the students understand? Where are their confusions? Which ideas are students grappling with? What is the logic in what they do? There were moments in this session when we were moving in the right direction, but there were plenty of moments when I felt frustrated that further thought was being blocked by what seemed to me too simple an analysis.

Here's the outline of the agenda: We spent 70 minutes on the case discussion: about 30 minutes in pairs, and about 40 minutes back together. The rest of the session was structured to help the teachers prepare for the mathematics interview they will be doing for homework before the next session. We looked at a 12-minute segment of videotaped interview—a teacher with a six-year-old child—and discussed the child's thinking. Then I rewound the tape, and we looked at it again, this time paying attention to the teacher: What type of questions is she asking? What is she trying to do? What kinds of information do her questions give her? Next I distributed, and we discussed, one teacher's write-up of her clinical interview. Finally, I put the teachers into grade-level groups to plan their own interviews. (Each teacher will be interviewing one of her own students.)

Case discussion: Getting everyone involved

Because the dynamics in this group have troubled me, I set up the discussion somewhat differently from the last two sessions. The conversation about norms notwithstanding, I've been concerned that some of the teachers are perceived as the ones who already understand "what this is about" and who speak up while the others listen. I don't want people to feel there's a "party line"; everyone's ideas need to be voiced if all are to have an equal opportunity to learn here. Nobody is bossy or mean or upset. It's just that some people tend to dominate the discussions and others are too ready to defer. To counter this, I wanted each person to come to whole-group discussion prepared to offer a point. When they got into small groups, I told them that they should share their ideas and that, before we get back together, each person should decide on one point to share with us all.

Now, after the lesson, I feel I made the right decision; it's important, at times, to create a space that allows everyone to speak. However, going around the circle with each person contributing also set up constraints on the discussion. It meant that, in the interest of reaching everyone, we couldn't get into anything very deeply. Perhaps this was one source of my frustration. Before I teach this seminar again, I'll try to come up with a strategy that both promotes deep thinking and also helps to make space for the quiet voices. These don't have to be in conflict.

As an example of what I found frustrating, Nadia started us off with an important point. She said that she was interested in the child [Mary, in case 13] whose representation of 127 with base ten blocks was 1 hundreds flat, 2 unit cubes, and 7 tens rods. She said she was puzzled because she didn't know what that child didn't understand. "Did she not get the ideas, or did she not understand how to use the blocks?"

I was thinking that Nadia's question would lead into the connection between written symbols—you've got 1 of something, 2 of something else, and 7 of still a third thing—and how they represent a single quantity. But instead, Patsy offered, "Maybe they haven't used the blocks enough; some teachers don't even use blocks." This comment shut down an exploration of the mathematical ideas, and the discussion turned into what the teacher should do to help the kids learn how to use the blocks. This is close to what I was frustrated with in last session's discussion of Janine's case. The notion that there are mathematical ideas the children might be exploring with the blocks seemed absent.

Another example arose over Dawn's case, "Number of Days in School" [case 11]. There was some discussion about whether a straight number line from 1 to 100 is more appropriate for kindergartners than the hundreds chart, but there was no reference to the importance of considering the ideas those kindergartners might be working on.

Now, I'm not saying that the teachers shouldn't be thinking about the value of different representations. The thing is, there are other issues to be considered *first*. I want them to learn how to use the cases to consider, for example, how the different representations might highlight various patterns that would help children begin to decide whether "5 and 10" or "sixty" follows 59. The insights the teachers gained from such investigations could then inform the decisions they make when confronted with situations like those described in the cases.

A more satisfying part of the discussion came from a point Claire made about Donna's case, "Groups and Leftovers" [case 12]. Donna had given her second graders an activity in which they grabbed handfuls of beans, divided them into groups of a specified size, and filled out a chart identifying the number in a group, the number of whole groups, the number of leftovers, and the total number. Claire reported she and the teachers in her group needed to do the activity together before they could see what was going on. After they figured out the mathematics, Claire had the following pedagogical insight: "Putting the beans into different-sized groups—it made me realize that I leave that out. If you just do tens, you don't see what is unusual about tens. That made me realize that sometimes I think I'm being open and discovery oriented, but I'm really looking for them to see this thing about ten, and so I set them up with 40 activities all about groups of ten. Then I feel like, 'Well, after all these activities, don't you see the pattern here?' But they never got to see when the pattern *doesn't* hold!"

It seemed to me that Claire had figured out something about the power of the system of tens—but also that the only way you can appreciate that power is to have the opportunity to explore, say, grouping by threes, sevens, and other amounts. Students need to think about lots of ways of grouping in order to notice what grouping by tens offers.

Yet, even though Claire is still talking about what the teacher does, why do I find her remarks more satisfying? Because she's talking about making different decisions, based on new insights about mathematics and about learning gained by engaging mathematics. That's what I'm after.

I also want to note that Claire's group did the activity Donna gave to her class. It feels good that they knew that would be a useful thing to do. Maybe I should have encouraged more groups to do just that. Perhaps if I had set things up so that small groups had all been focused on doing the mathematics in that one case, the whole-group discussion would have been more grounded in mathematical thinking.

Preparing for the math interview

Before turning on the videotape, I let the teachers read the portfolio assignment describing the interviews they will be conducting before our next meeting. I explained what they would be doing to prepare: first looking at a videotaped interview; then reading a teacher's interview write-up; and finally, getting into groups to plan their interviews.

On the video, the teacher, Jill, is interviewing a six-year-old boy named Chris. The interview took place the summer before Chris entered first grade. Jill had not met Chris before the day of the interview and so, in that way, her situation differs from that of the teachers in the group.

I said that we would be viewing the tape to learn what Chris understands about numbers, and I suggested that they might want to take notes. As we watched the tape, it seemed the teachers were quite taken by Chris. He is cute and is thinking very hard.

I intended to organize the discussion about Chris in two parts. First we would talk about what Chris did—get our facts straight. Then we would make inferences about what Chris understood. So I started our discussion by asking, "What observations can we make about what Chris did?"

Joan said, "He knows how to count to 61. And he said he could count to 100."

Patsy added, "He can count higher than that. When Jill started him at 105, he counted to 119 before she stopped him."

Nadia said, "And he could count from wherever Jill asked him to start."

Carla offered, "Chris knows that it matters which way you write a number, but he doesn't always get it right."

I had wanted to separate observations of what Chris did from our inferences of what he understood, but I found that was hard to do. Instead of pointing out to Carla that she was making an inference instead of an observation, I asked, "What do you mean?"

"Well, like, when he wrote 24. First, he wrote the 4 backward, but he knew it was backward and corrected it. Then when he wrote 31, he got the 3 backward but didn't know it."

I was interested that Carla attended to the way Chris wrote individual numerals but didn't mention the order of digits in a multidigit number. When I asked a question about that, Sheila, who was clearly agitated, blurted out, "I think that teacher was being really unfair! He was trying really hard and he was getting tired and she was asking questions that were unfair!"

I asked Sheila what she meant; what was Jill doing that was unfair? She explained, "Why is she asking a child who is just out of kindergarten questions about numbers that are so big? How is he supposed to get the right answers if he hasn't been taught those things? You don't learn about place value in kindergarten."

This was another surprise for me. Sheila seemed unable to look for evidence of how Chris understood such notions as place value. Instead, she had been watching to see what he could answer correctly and where he was mistaken. To Sheila, a wrong answer would reflect badly on either Chris or Jill. I guess she thought that asking Chris to write numbers like 31 was fair, even though he wrote some of the numerals backward, but asking him to write numbers larger than 100 was unfair.

I heard some other voices ready to jump on Jill, but I decided to postpone that discussion. "In a minute we'll have a discussion about what the interviewer did, but for now let's stay focused on Chris. What was going on when he tried to write numbers larger than 100?"

Patsy, Marta, Claire, and Joan had ideas about this. They all seemed pretty intrigued by what Chris had to say about one thousand five.

"He knew to write one thousand as 1000 and said it has 'three O's.' And he knew that for one thousand five, the 5 replaces one of those zeros but he didn't know which one."

"Yeah, and the same thing came up for one hundred two. He knew 1 would be at the left, and he knew there would be a 0 and a 2, but he didn't know which order to put them in."

"So he knows that order is important," Joan added. "But he doesn't know the right order yet."

I asked if it would help to look at the video again, now concentrating on the interviewer's questions. There was a low rumble of dissatisfaction, but I couldn't quite tell where it was coming from. Because the loudest voices insisted they wanted to look at the tape again—and because I, too, thought that would be a good idea—I let the loudest voices prevail.

After the second viewing, Sheila was quiet, so I didn't know where she was at this point. Marta started us off, "I was really interested in how Jill's questions progressed. She began by asking him to count. It was something he could do very well and it was a way to build his confidence. That was a good way to start."

Patsy said, "When she asked him to write numbers, she started with 8 and then went up to larger and harder numbers."

Nadia added, "I was pretty interested in the question, 'What is the biggest number you know?' Chris wasn't sure what she meant, if it was the biggest number he could count to or the biggest number he could name. And Jill said he could answer both questions."

I wanted to underscore that exchange, so I said, "Chris pointed out to us that there are lots of different ways to know something. You can think about knowing a number if you can count up to it, or if you can say it, or if you can write it. Remember, he could say 'one million,' but didn't know how to write it; he could write 1000. Are there other ways to think about knowing numbers?"

I don't know if anyone thought about that question. Marjorie went on to say, "I noticed that when Chris was counting on from 28, he said '28, 29, 40, 41, 42.' Jill didn't tell him he was wrong, and she acted exactly the same way as when he got it right. But she gave him another chance and started him at 25. The next time, he did it right."

Tammy said, "Yeah, she did the same thing when he was writing numbers. She didn't react when he wrote his numerals backward. And when he didn't know where to place the 5 to write 1005, she didn't give him any clues."

Shannon asked, "Is that good? I mean, we're teachers. Aren't we supposed to tell the kids what's right? How are they supposed to learn?"

I said that Shannon's question was a good one. "We should think about when it's important for a teacher to tell students how to do things. [As I said this, I saw Sheila make an exasperated gesture, but I went on.] However, it would be useful, for the purpose of this assignment, not to think about teaching. Instead, you're trying to figure out what your student understands about numbers. What is it that you can do as the interviewer to get the most information?"

Shannon sort of nodded and shrugged. No one seemed to have anything else to say about this, so we moved on. I handed out the interview write-up of a second grader named Nick, gave the group a few minutes to read it, and then asked, "What strikes you about Nick?"

Marta said, "You know, it's interesting to read about this child after thinking about all the other kids in the cases and stuff. We can see that Nick knows how to show his numbers with base ten blocks. He doesn't mix up what the flats and rods stand for [as in Marie's case 13]. But sometimes he writes a number with too many zeros in it. That's what we saw with some of the kids in the cases [e.g., Danielle's case 15]."

When Marta said that, I felt like kissing her! This is exactly what I want teachers to see—that once you start paying attention to children's ideas about the mathematics, even though each child is unique and some children's ideas are idiosyncratic, there are patterns in what they do and say. I also want them to start seeing how the ideas we're looking at in this seminar are connected. Right now we're investigating the ways kids start to understand (or are confused about) different aspects of the base ten structure of numbers. We'll return to how that understanding is employed when the children invent procedures for multidigit addition and subtraction, and later we'll look at multiplication and division and do some work with decimals. Well, it seems that Marta might be on her way to seeing this.

But I felt that, in front of the group, I shouldn't make too big a deal of Marta's contribution. If people start to feel that she has the "right answer," it's likely that they'll stop coming forward with their own ideas and questions. So, instead, I asked, "Any other thoughts?"

Tomi brought me back to the interview write-up: "She started out writing about what the class was doing, not about the interview. Is that what we're supposed to do?"

I responded that it was useful for this teacher to explain why she interviewed Nick, but they could start out just writing about the interview, if that's what works for them.

We didn't have much more discussion about the interview write-up. I handed out this sample mainly to show what their portfolio assignment might look like. Until now, the only model the teachers had for writing about student thinking was the cases—but I didn't want them to think they would have to transcribe a 30-minute interview to capture the child's words verbatim. Rather, I wanted them to go over their interview and write about what they learned: "I was surprised when the student did this, and I had to ask this other question to see what was going on . . ." or "It made me realize . . ."

Group planning for the interviews

At 6:20 P.M. I asked the teachers to get into grade-level groups. I believed that this planning time would be important for several reasons.

First, I thought the teachers would be a little nervous about planning an interview, which seems a bit funny since they talk with students all the time. But working with one student, taping the conversation, and then listening to it and analyzing it—that's different from what they've ever done before.

I also figured the teachers would feel better if they could get into groups to plan some of the questions they could use to get started. But I also wanted them to understand that, even if you plan a set of questions, once the conversation gets started, you want to respond to what the student is saying and doing. They mustn't feel bound to the questions they prepare.

I suggested the teachers flip back through all the cases we've discussed in our first three meetings. They should think about the various mathematical issues that come up in the cases, identify some they find particularly interesting, and design questions that would help them learn about where their own student is on those issues. My intention was to have grade-level groups start with the same set of questions so that in the next session they could compare their findings.

After discussing the questions they would like to ask in their interviews, the teachers came together so that we could get a sense of the range of issues the group planned to explore. Beginning with the lower and going up through the higher grades, each group identified either the mathematical issue they were curious about or the questions they would open with.

I then suggested each teacher think of one thing that was new to her in this seminar and resolve to use her interview as an opportunity to experiment with it. Shannon said that she had never used manipulatives before and so she wanted to see what her student would make of base ten blocks. Nadia said it might be hard, but she was going to try *not* to show her student how to do the problems she would pose but, instead, listen to the child's way of doing things.

Session 4
More on addition and subtraction
of two-digit numbers

Maxine's Journal

October 23

As usual, I have mixed feelings about last night's session, but this time I'm not sure what's making me uneasy. A lot has happened—things that excited me and things that disappointed me—and I'm feeling pretty jumbled. Maybe as I write, some of it will get sorted out.

It was actually quite a full session—sharing experiences from interviewing students, discussing the cases, viewing a video, and doing some mental arithmetic. I managed the time as follows: 1 hour on the interviews (30 minutes in small group and 30 minutes in whole group); 45 minutes discussing the cases; a 15-minute break; 45 minutes viewing and discussing the video; and 15 minutes on mental math.

Discussing the interviews

We began the session sharing what happened in the student interviews. First, the teachers got into the same small groups they were in last week when they planned their interviews. Having worked on their questions together, they could now compare notes on what happened.

I went around, listening in on groups to get a sense of where people were, and I learned that they were all over the place. Despite the discussion we had at our last meeting, some teachers couldn't separate this interview task from teaching, and their vision of teaching *didn't* involve eliciting students' ideas. There were teachers who couldn't separate being successful teachers from having their students get the problem right. Tomi felt the need to report to me that she stayed with her student until she straightened him out. And Sheila seemed to be at the same place as last time—she would never ask a question of a student unless she were quite sure the student could answer it correctly; it's unfair to ask something you haven't already taught; and so forth. Her interpretation of the interview assignment was, first explain the task to the child, and then ask questions to make sure he does it right.

So, what does it mean that it's the fourth session and some people still don't have an inkling of what it means to examine student thinking? Am I doing something wrong? Is there something I can do so that they'll get it? As I write this, I realize that there's a parallel here between how I'm feeling and the position I put them in when I assigned these interviews. Here I am, panicked (and that's only a slight exaggeration) that there are teachers in the group who just aren't getting it—they had this big assignment, and they didn't do it right. And that makes me think that maybe I'm a lousy teacher, maybe this seminar is a flop. At the same time, I am telling them to interview students and discover the ways they think about the mathematics. So they interview students and discover that they just don't get all those things they had been taught. And how does that make the teachers feel? Lousy. This isn't just an intellectual exercise. A teacher is compelled to act on what she learns about her students, and so it makes sense that some of these teachers avoid learning things they don't know how to act on.

Hence, that issue comes back to me. What can *I* do? What can I do to make it safe enough for these teachers to begin to discover something about student thinking? And to make them begin to see that teaching involves listening to their students' mathematical ideas?

To answer my questions, I can apply exactly what I want the teachers to learn. What I can do is listen hard to what the teachers are saying—listen to their mathematical ideas as well as their ideas about teaching and learning. But where, in all that, can I find elements of strength in their ideas that can be highlighted and leveraged to help them reconsider some of their own notions?

I started out by saying that the group was all over the place. Some people really are starting to get it. As I listened in on the small groups, I was also taking account of the mathematical issues that were coming up and some of the points were right on target—teachers were uncovering the kind of student insights and confusions that can help fill out the picture of what we're studying this semester. Having heard some of these points in small groups, I tried to make sure they would be raised in our whole-group discussion.

When we came together, I asked people to recount specific mathematical points that had come up in their interviews. To show them what I meant, I shared one that I had heard: When Joan asked her student to write the numeral *nine hundred fifty-eight,* the child wrote 900508. "We all know that this is incorrect," I said. "But can we see the child's logic? In what way does this make sense?"

It was easy for people to articulate why this might make sense. By now, some of the teachers seem to be quite clear that the spoken system for representing numbers is different from the written system; the mistake this child made came from trying to translate the spoken system into written symbols without understanding the principles of the written system. The work that many of the group still need to do involves sorting out for themselves those very principles and coming to see how much thinking children need to do to understand them.

In response to Joan's example and the discussion about how we can understand the logic in what the child did, Shannon said, "My students are so uncreative, they would never do anything like that." I'm not sure what to make of this comment. Shannon was one of the teachers who, in the first session, told me that she was a traditional teacher and might not belong in this seminar. Now she's actually talking as though it would be positive if her students were to make this error; she seems to see it as a display of creativity. And what is this declaration that her students aren't creative? Was she condemning the school system? the students? Or is this a way to get herself off the hook? If she can simply say that her students are not creative, that they don't think this way, then she doesn't have to change the way she teaches. As a consequence, her students would be shut off from powerful ideas.

Anyway, the discussion went on. Marjorie talked about her very confident student who, when asked to write one thousand ten, wrote 1, left a space on the page, then wrote 10—that is, "1 10." Marjorie asked the girl to put a zero in the space, but the child replied she didn't need to because zero doesn't mean anything.

Tammy said that when she asked her student to write ninety-eight, he wrote 908, and then looked at it and said, "No, that's wrong; it's way too big."

What does it mean to say that one child understands place value and that another doesn't? As these two anecdotes illustrate, when we ask questions about what might be going on behind the answers children give, whether right or wrong, we begin to realize just how complex place value is.

Claire reported that she asked her student to count and, although he could count pretty high, it started to feel as though he was saying the numbers without any sense of system or structure. Some people began to talk about whether a kid sees, say, 13, as though it's a single digit and not something that can be decomposed. Claire said she was pretty surprised when she realized that her student didn't have any idea how 13 could be broken up. I asked what the child could have done to make her feel confident he did have that idea. As Claire pondered the question, Patsy said she would feel satisfied if the child could represent 13 as a ten-rod and three unit-cubes. Marta said that she wasn't sure; she'd feel better if the child separated Unifix cubes as 10 and 3. "I'm not sure why. With the base ten blocks, it seems as if it's already done *for* them."

Several teachers brought up issues about whether their students understood the placement of commas in large numbers. I didn't really know what to do with that. I'm not used to thinking about the comma as a mathematical object, but for several teachers and their students, there seemed to be something significant here.

So, there were a few people in the group who were able to use the interview assignment to get at some of their students' thinking. They weren't terrified to discover confusions. In fact, most were intrigued by the patterns the group was finding.

As an aside, Nadia mentioned that when she was doing the interview, she didn't notice the noise level in the room. (She explained that she did the interview in the classroom while someone else took over the class.) It sounded as if this was a shift for her, that she's someone who tends to worry if the class gets noisy. Now she's wondering if noise doesn't really bother the students as much as it bothers her. She said she was thinking that maybe it doesn't seem noisy to students if they are engaged in something and really concentrating on what they're doing.

Case discussion: The purple way

The two cases in chapter 4 differ from those the group has read previously, in that they were written in consecutive years by the same second-grade teacher. In the first case, Lynn reflects on her class work on place value and two-digit computation; she raises some pretty big questions about the use of various mathematical representations and the role of the historically taught "trading" algorithms in her curriculum. In Lynn's second case, she doesn't address those issues as directly, but her description of what was going on in her class suggests some of her own answers. I didn't think this group was ready to take on these issues the way Lynn does, but I did want them to look carefully at some short segments of her cases in order to think about children's methods for adding and subtracting. I saw these cases as offering a review, returning to the ideas introduced in chapter 1. I asked the group to address the first two focus questions before coming together for the whole-group discussion.

As I listened in on small groups, I noticed the teachers were fairly fluent in applying to 46 + 37 the five procedures Lynn had on her poster. The ideas that had seemed so foreign at our first meeting fit rather comfortably by now. Even without my asking, some groups were doing the same thing with the second case—that is, they tested each of the children's procedures with different numbers to see if everyone in the group agreed on what the procedure was.

When we gathered as a whole group, we no longer needed to duplicate the students' procedures. So instead, I asked, "As you revisit these methods for adding multidigit numbers, can you make any assumptions about what children understand when they use them?"

Some members of the group were able to address this question by now. Claire said, "I think about my little guy, the child I interviewed, who didn't see 13 as 1 ten and 3 ones. I don't think he would come up with the green way, the blue way, or the red way. If he can add numbers that large, he'd do it the purple way."

I thought it was pretty interesting that Claire didn't even mention the pink way, the algorithm that is usually taught in U.S. schools. I also wanted to make sure that other members of the group understood what Claire was talking about. "What do you think about what Claire said? What does 13 have to do with these procedures?"

Tammy spoke up. "Those three ways have to do with breaking numbers apart into tens and ones. Children don't necessarily see that. I remember working on a case last time [Donna's case 12], where the kids picked out a handful of beans and divided them into groups. They began to see a pattern when they put the beans into groups of ten; it was connected to how the number was written. The kids have to get that, in order to add those ways."

I really liked this part of the discussion. Yes, this is what I wanted teachers to notice. But I was aware that several others remained silent. What was

Sheila thinking? What about Tomi? And Amira was always so quiet—what's going on with her?

Patsy interjected, "You know, the green way reminds me of algebra."

Algebra? I didn't quite see it, so I asked her what she meant.

She replied, "I don't know. It just seems like it. You know, adding like terms."

I moved on. "What do you think about what Fiona [case 17] was doing with the pigeons, when she was subtracting?"

Joan said, "I don't know, I thought she was amazing. It had never occurred to me how hard it is to think about this stuff. When I was trying to follow what she was doing, I wasn't sure if she was supposed to add or subtract that last part."

"What is it that helped Fiona sort it out?" I asked.

Joan continued, "Well, the teacher said it was when she asked Fiona if those birds stayed or flew away."

Joan certainly got a lot out of that case, but as I looked around, I was still concerned about those silent people. How was I going to bring them in? Should I stick with this discussion or turn to the video? The video might get at some of these same ideas about how children decompose numbers and keep track of how to recombine them when adding and subtracting. And maybe the video would draw more folks in. So that's what I decided to do.

Discussing the video: Why teach the algorithm?

As the discussion of Lynn's cases wound down, I asked the group to get their snacks and sit down again for the video. Like the other tapes we've seen, this one provides images of real students in real time. However, it offers more than the earlier ones. Even though this video was designed to explore issues related to the first half of *Building a System of Tens*—students making sense of the base ten structure of number and using that understanding to add and subtract multidigit numbers—it also presents classroom scenes and interviews with the teachers, and the narrator offers interpretation.

The video lasted a little over 20 minutes, and after it ended, there was silence. Finally, Helen said, "Why do we teach the algorithm if kids can figure it out on their own?" But then she asked, "On the other hand, don't they really need to know how to do the algorithm for standardized tests?" In fact, Helen's first question was the one Lynn had taken on in her cases, and I hadn't wanted to push the teachers into thinking about this. But now that Helen had posed the question, there were several people who were willing to tackle it.

The ensuing discussion was rather interesting. "If you get the right answer on a standardized test, does anyone know how you got it?"

"If you know the standard algorithm, does it mean that you get the right answer faster?"

"Maybe if you use your own algorithm, it's faster *and* more reliable."

At this point in this group's process, it seemed OK that these issues came up. As teachers begin to pose questions for themselves, their ideas are fragmented and preliminary. If they choose, the seminar will offer plenty of opportunity to continue to ponder them. Because this is a controversial set of questions with serious policy implications, and because parents are likely to have their own strong opinions, it is a good idea for teachers to explore all sides of these issues.

On another topic, Claire mentioned that she was relieved when one of the teachers on the video said that at first she didn't get what one of her students was doing when he explained his method of solving a subtraction problem. After she said that, a number of teachers went, "Yeah!" It seemed as though they all felt some relief there. They said that they, too, had been confused; the child hadn't done what they expected him to do. But then, when the teacher asked him to back up and explain again exactly what he was doing as she recorded it on the board, they were able to follow along with her.

More mental math

I suggested that we do some mental math again. First I gave them 69 + 23, and we discussed their methods; then they did 132 − 85. As they shared their approaches, three different teachers indicated they were now thinking this way only after studying children's strategies in this seminar. "Before I would have just done the pencil-and-paper way in my head. Now I'm more flexible." This type of comment was really exciting for me to hear.

Then I introduced some multiplication, wanting to prepare the teachers for the cases they'd be reading for homework: 29×6, 16×3, and 153×2. After we discussed solution strategies for these, I asked if the word *array* was familiar. It was clear from their nervous laughter that, although they had heard the word, some of the teachers did not know what it meant. I asked for a definition, and Patsy offered: "An arrangement like a rectangle." As she spoke, she gestured in the air to show 3 rows of 5 dots each.

Helen added, "3 by 5." I asked Helen to come to the easel to show us, and she drew this:

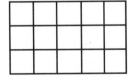

I wanted this language to be clear because arrays are used in some of the cases in the next chapter of the casebook.

Maxine's Journal

November 6

Last night's session feels like a breakthrough! Finally, we were all working together on a set of ideas, and I wasn't having to try so hard to show the group where to look, what to notice, or even *how* to notice. It's not as if *everyone* has gone through a transformation since the last session. But at this point I sense that, as a group, we have a shared understanding of what we're about and what we're doing when we come together for three hours every other week. People are learning how to explore a piece of mathematics for themselves, and they are starting to figure out how to read the cases to learn about children's thinking. Hurray!

The work in this chapter on multiplication was quite challenging for everyone in the group, and we spent a good long while looking at the mathematics itself before turning to the cases. It was important that the teachers had a chance to sort out some of their own mathematical issues before trying to figure out what the children were doing. We then spent an hour on the cases, leaving us with 30 minutes at the end of the session to view the video.

Math activity: Exploring multidigit multiplication

I actually started to feel encouraged even before we got started. Marta walked in, sat down at a desk, smiled, and started talking to me across the room. "You know," she said, "before this class, I never had discussions in math. I always had discussions in all my other subjects. Why didn't I ever think of having a discussion in math?" Her question was rhetorical; I didn't have to answer.

Then, Marta's comment notwithstanding, I started to pick up some tension. I tried several times to bring folks together, but they seemed unwilling to sit down and stop talking. When, at last, I got their attention and said I thought we'd spend the first part of the session figuring out for ourselves some things about multiplication, there was a shift in the mood. It was as if most of the class had been avoiding looking at me, and now they looked up. I guess they thought I assumed they understood the mathematics in the cases, and they were dreading three hours of trying to pull off a discussion about this stuff. Once it became clear to them that we were going to start by doing some work to help them figure out the mathematics, they were relieved. And then they really got into it!

I put the teachers in groups of three and explained that I wanted them to make models for 16×18 using diagrams (graph paper was available), base ten blocks, Cuisenaire rods, and cubes; I further requested that they try to use each of these materials in more than one way.

It seemed that many of the teachers had never before had a mental image for a product as large as 16 × 18. They thought of multiplication as repeated addition—16 + 16 + 16 + . . . + 16—but that's hard to picture. They could picture something like 3 × 4 as three groups of four:

But 16 groups of 18 is too hard to hold onto until it gets organized into an array. So I think it was actually pleasurable for the teachers to expand their image of multiplication this way.

The teachers took a while to sort out how to represent the problem with base ten blocks. Some started by pulling out a rod and six units to represent 16 and a rod and eight units to represent 18, and then just sat there. They didn't know how to connect that to multiplication. When I noticed this, I asked that they think of a situation in which they would multiply 16 × 18. When they suggested, "There are 16 kids and each has 18 lollipops," they realized that they needed *sixteen* 18s, not just *one* 16 and *one* 18. That brought them to this arrangement:

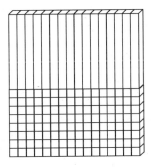

Most groups did not think of trading ten rods for a flat or groups of ten cubes for rods; they were satisfied that their representation gave them the right answer: 288. (With all the work we've done on decomposing numbers, these groups did not look for the 2 hundreds, 8 tens, and 8 ones.) However, some people in the class came up with this arrangement:

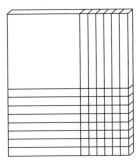

They didn't use the term "partial product" as they talked, but I think this is what they were seeing here. When I came over to the group, they showed me how the flat represented 10×10, the rods came from 6×10 and 10×8, and the unit cubes were the 6×8. I suggested that they write all that out: $16 \times 18 = 10 \times 10 + 6 \times 10 + 10 \times 8 + 6 \times 8$. As Marta stared at the page and then looked back at the blocks, she realized, "Wouldn't children who learned multiplication this way have an easy time in algebra?" I asked her what she meant, and she said, "You know, it looks like what we did in algebra. All that 'foil' stuff."

No one else in the group was making Marta's connection, and my guess was that more discussion about it wouldn't help. But I am interested in Marta's recognizing this bit from her Algebra I course: $(a + b) \times (c + d) = ac + ad + bc + bd$. That is, algebra texts often give the rule for multiplying binomials: multiply *first* terms, *outer* terms, *inner* terms, and *last* terms (the initial of each adjective gives *foil*, a mnemonic to help students remember the order). It's really just applying the distributive property twice. Anyway, I guess Marta was seeing that you could look at 16×18 as $(10 + 6) \times (10 + 8)$, a case of $(a + b) \times (c + d)$, and the blocks could be separated to show each of the four resulting products. It's not so much the specifics of the insight I'm interested in, but rather that she is beginning to recognize how ideas are connected. If her second graders start to examine how numbers work, their future studies—for example, of algebra—will make more sense to them.

For now, I wasn't so concerned whether everyone else would connect multiplication of two-digit numbers to multiplication of binomials, but I do want them all to become aware of their own mathematical insights and how they come about, and to consider implications for their students.

I was interested in what was going on in a group working with Cuisenaire rods. They explained to me that they used the base ten blocks first, but once they came up with one arrangement, they couldn't see another way of laying out the blocks; this set of materials felt constraining. So they went to the Cuisenaire rods and laid out a 16×18 array using 9-rods. That is, they made up 18 by laying two 9-rods end-to-end and lined up 16 of those. Then, taking up the challenge to find another way to use the materials, they moved the bottom row of 9-rods up next to the other row to create a 32×9 array. They were intrigued that they could halve one of the numbers, double the other, and the product would stay the same.

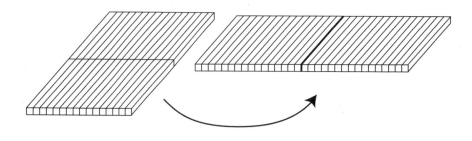

Building a System of Tens

I asked them to try other arrangements of Cuisenaire rods. For instance, what if they made their 16 × 18 array out of 8-rods? What if they made it out of 6-rods? Using the same blocks, would they be able to come up with another rectangular arrangement?

I like where this group is now—learning to use various materials to represent operations, beginning to notice things in those representations, and becoming curious about the mathematics. Eventually, I would want to be able to push their observations further. "Given that you're starting with a 16 × 18 array, what are *all* the other possible arrays, assuming that the sides are whole numbers? What if you start with a 7 × 13 array? What about a 9 × 15 array? What generalizations can you make?" This issue of learning to articulate generalizations and developing vocabulary and a symbol system for it is important, but that comes later. As I said, for now I'm satisfied with what they're doing.

I was also interested in what Nadia's group was doing, but at the time I missed the boat—as I've been thinking back about what was going on, I recognize a set of issues that would have been worthwhile to explore more deeply. Here's what happened:

Nadia was thinking that she'd apply a procedure like one of those we'd used with addition. Take 2 from the 16 and add it to the 18: 14 × 20 = 280. Why didn't it give them the right answer? They had already used other procedures to solve the problem, and they knew the answer was 288. She and her group were puzzled about this. Eventually I suggested that they try to see what was going on with the blocks. What if they started with a 16 × 18 array, and tried to turn it into a 14 × 20 array?

But it's a lot of blocks to move around, and it got pretty cumbersome, so Joan suggested they try to draw it on graph paper. She shaded in a 16 × 18 array and then took some scissors and cut off two columns, resulting in a 14 × 18 and a 2 × 18 array. Then she took the two-column array and added it at the bottom of the larger array.

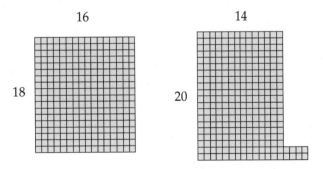

From this, they could see that moving the columns into rows wasn't going to conserve the quantity. In the end, they had those eight extra cubes sticking out. I suggested they make up similar problems with other numbers to see what happens.

Since the session, I've been thinking a lot about what Nadia's group was doing—trying to solve a multiplication problem by applying a procedure that works for addition—and I realize this happens pretty frequently in the classroom. It shows up in both the print and video cases. In Susannah's second case [case 21], Josh tries to solve 12×18 by computing $10 \times 10 + 2 \times 8 = 100 + 16$. After all, we've been looking at children who, when given a problem like $12 + 18$, will separate out the tens and ones ($10 + 10 = 20$ and $2 + 8 = 10$) and then add the results, and that gives them the right answer! So why not with multiplication? Also, on the video, Thomas H was working on 36×17. He said he wanted to round up to the nearest tens, $40 \times 20 = 800$, and then subtract off the 4 and the 3 he had added on, giving him the result of 793, which is wrong. His method does work for addition: $36 + 17 = 40 + 20 - 4 - 3 = 53$.

I think this piece of mathematics is very important and would have been useful for the group to think about. Why do such procedures work for addition but not multiplication? What does it have to do with what multiplication *is*? In the case discussion that followed, no one even mentioned Josh's error. And after the teachers viewed the video toward the end of the session, they spent the rest of the time trying to figure out what happens to the problem when you apply Thomas's procedure. Next time I teach this seminar, I'll design the math activity to make sure these questions come up. If the teachers explore such questions in the context of the math activity, then maybe we can have a rich discussion of Josh's and Thomas's errors.

Before I move on to the case discussion, I want to write about something that happened during small group time, unrelated to the mathematics task I had set up. Velma called me over to show me one of her student's papers. "Look," she said, "today one of my students did something like what the kids in the cases are doing. I'm so excited." I looked at the page: It involved multiplication, and the child had used the analogy that four quarters make a dollar to conclude that 4×25 must be 100. I didn't quite get what Velma was saying, so I asked in what way it's like the cases. "Well, I never taught her that. She just made it up. I wonder why she did that. I mean, is it because of the new book, or did I just happen to see it today?"

I take from this that Velma is learning in this course that children can invent their own methods for solving problems without the teacher having to show them first. As she takes this insight into her classroom, she starts to notice that *her* students, too, invent their own methods. At this point she's wondering how this happened ("Is it because of the new book . . .?"). My own question is whether she'll realize that, as a teacher, she can learn to leverage her students' independent thinking to help them investigate mathematics more deeply.

At 5 P.M. I called the group together. Most people shared the observations recounted above. There was one new point: In the middle of the discussion, Marjorie became excited when she realized she could map the conventional algorithm onto the way she had arranged her blocks.

$$\begin{array}{r} 16 \\ \times\,18 \\ \hline 128 \\ \underline{160} \\ 288 \end{array}$$

She pointed out how the 160 is represented by the 16 rods and the 128 is represented by all the cubes underneath.

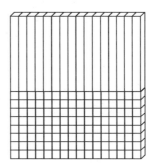

Case discussion: The logic of student thinking

When I asked the teachers to get into small groups to look at the cases in chapter 5, they knew exactly what to do. I suggested that they begin by looking closely at what the students were doing in Eleanor's case, "27 × 4, or Dogs Looking for Scraps" [case 18], and I was quite impressed by the care and attention they applied to this task. I went around and listened and didn't intervene—and these are some of the things I heard:

HELEN: Look, she added the 4 × 63 and the 8 × 63 to get the 12 × 63. I knew I could figure it out.

SHANNON: But wouldn't it have been easier to just do 6 × 63 and double it?

HELEN: Not for her. She must have been using what was familiar to her.

And a few minutes later:

SHANNON: The way Jen did 14 × 16—she kept building up from pieces she knew, and she could keep track to see how many more she needed.

HELEN: She does that with the next one, too.

SHANNON: It looks like these kids use what they think they already know to do these new problems.

These teachers are assuming that the students in the cases apply logic as they engage the mathematics, and if they, the teachers, try, they will be able to figure out what the students are doing. Furthermore, it requires that they, themselves, develop mathematical facility. For example, Helen needs to recognize how $4 \times 63 = 252$ and $8 \times 63 = 504$ can be used to find the product of 12×63.

I'm impressed by Shannon's last comment: "It looks like these kids use what they think they already know to do these new problems." That's a concise description of an important aspect of how learning takes place, and an insight that's not generally shared among teachers. It *is* an insight that I'm hoping everyone in the seminar will come to before long. I did hear it from another group of three:

CARLA: It just amazes me that they think of all these ways. I would never have been able to. I'm so traditional. I would never have thought to do all of this.

MARJORIE: So then I wonder, are some of the kids sitting out there thinking like this?

VELMA: I wonder, when do they start making these shortcuts on their own? It's amazing. Where are they getting this?

In fact, this is what Velma was saying, too, as she showed me her student's work. Velma is beginning to notice that her own students, her very own students, think in ways similar to the children she has been reading about. Marjorie also seems to suspect this may be the case. But I'm sensitive to the fact that Shannon says "these kids," meaning the kids in the cases. I wonder when she will begin thinking about *her* students.

After 20 minutes, I called people together for the whole-group discussion. Before we started in, people said that going back to the cases *after* doing the mathematics for themselves in the first part of the session made the episodes seem totally different. They said they were able to figure out a lot more about what was going on with the kids than when they read the cases at home.

I asked people what they learned from working with these cases. Was there anything that was particularly enlightening?

Patsy said that she was intrigued with what was going on when Jen [in case 18] worked on 14×16. Jen calculated two 14s (28), three 14s (42), six 14s (84), seven 14s (103), fourteen 14s (206), and sixteen 14s (234). "The thing is," Patsy said, "Jen's thinking was perfect. Her answer was wrong but her strategy was right." Patsy pointed out that Jen just made a mistake in one step when she added, going from six 14s to seven 14s. "Compared with everything right she was doing, that mistake is pretty trivial."

At this point, the conversation diverged from the case.

Velma said, "So what do you do when a student has a great method but makes a trivial mistake like that? Do you call attention to the mistake?"

Marta responded, "I wouldn't want the mistake to be left, but I also don't want to denigrate the student's work by calling attention to the error."

Then Claire said, "But look, if kids share their ways with other kids and the other kids are really trying to figure out what they did, wouldn't that just come up? Wouldn't some other kid just say, look you added wrong there. And it would just get fixed. It wouldn't be a big deal like the teacher saw you make a mistake."

I'm remembering my agitation several weeks ago when people weren't thinking hard about the mathematics students learn—they skipped past that and went right to teaching strategies. Here's an example of talk about strategies based on the mathematics they want students to learn. This feels better.

Turning back to the case, Helen pointed out that the first time Jen tried, she wrote 2 + 2 = 4, but she meant that two of the 27s plus two more 27s equals four 27s. "How can this child keep the groups in her head? It's hard for me, as an adult, to keep track, and this child doesn't seem to have any trouble doing it!"

"It's hard for us to follow, but it's not hard for the kid who comes up with the idea."

At this point, Carla began to reminisce about the New Math days, the reform movement of a few decades back. "Some of what we were supposed to teach was like this. What's different is, back then we were supposed to present the ideas and the students were supposed to remember them. Here, the ideas are coming from the students." Then there was a long pause. It felt as though folks were taking this in.

Then I asked the group to turn to Susannah's case, "Confusion over Multiplication" [case 20]. Before we got into the mathematics, people said they really liked that case. It felt good to read about a teacher who was struggling, where every intervention was just making matters worse. It was an acknowledgment that teaching is hard and often frustrating. They felt close to Susannah.

I asked the class to look specifically at Susannah's student, Michael. He had come up with a way to multiply 12×3 by separating 12 into 10 and 2 and multiplying each part by 3. When Michael tried to apply the same method to 25×9, he confused his carrying rules and got 854 (instead of 225). The first thing I wanted the teachers to do was to figure out how Michael came to 854. It took them a long time to sort it out, but they did. I think it was a powerful moment when they realized Michael wasn't just writing down numbers randomly. He was following a flawed procedure, but with elements of correct logic.

The thing is, at first the teachers had trouble seeing which part of Michael's procedure was correct. I asked the group if they could apply Michael's strategy to *correctly* solve 25×9, and everyone said no. They couldn't separate Michael's correct logic from his methods of recording, which had broken down. When I asked them to apply Michael's method without his recording errors, they reread the line from the case: "I separated the 20 over here and the 5 over here." When the teachers then multiplied the 20×9 and the 5×9, they were surprised to come up with the correct answer!

This was interesting to me, because all Michael was doing was applying the distributive property as they had been doing for the last couple of hours. But in this context, the idea of breaking apart the number and then multiplying seemed foreign to them. Apparently the work they had done with the manipulatives didn't immediately translate to Michael's work on paper. I'm sure that if, separate from Susannah's case, I had asked them if I could get 25 × 9 from multiplying 9 × 20 and 9 × 5, they would have said yes. Somehow, here, the method of recording got mixed up with what it meant to multiply. So this was useful, and people were excited to find out that this would work.

The only comment about Lauren's case, "Multiplication Cluster Problems" [case 19], came from Marjorie. She said it really bothered her that, here it was March, and this fourth-grade class was still doing one-digit multiplication. Patsy spoke up in response and suggested that sometimes when you introduce a new idea, you want to back up to what the kids already know. Maybe they're looking at 23 × 4 so that they could move on to 23 × 14. Marjorie seemed to be listening hard. I think that, to Marjorie, multiplying by one digit and multiplying by two digits have always been different topics. After all, they do appear in different chapters in many textbooks. It was a revelation to think that you could learn about two-digit multiplication by looking at one-digit multiplication.

Viewing the video: Thomas's procedure

Time was getting short, so I turned on the video. Again, it was important for the teachers to have visual images that match the print cases. In the video, we see third and fifth graders working through procedures that are quite similar to those the teachers were just working on in the math activity.

One new strategy presented in the video involves rounding factors to the nearest ten, multiplying, and then compensating at the end. A fifth grader, Jemea, solves 29 × 12 correctly when she rounds the single factor, 29, to 30. She adds twelve 30s to get 360 and subtracts off 12 to get 348. However, Thomas complicates his problem, 36 × 17, by rounding up *both* of his factors. He adds 4 to 36 to get 40, and 3 to 17 to get 20. Then he multiplies 40 × 20, getting 800, and subtracts off the 4 and 3 he originally added, getting 793.

The teacher on the video has Thomas H present his procedure to the class (even though he already knows it is incorrect) and asks the class, for homework, to think about what is going on here. What is Thomas's method, and how would you change it to make it work? End of video. So now the teachers in the seminar took on that task for themselves.

This took us to the end of class, and nobody had sorted out the ideas, though some folks were intrigued. I told them that, just as the children in the video had this as a homework assignment, they could think about it at home, too. Marjorie made a joke about being mad at Thomas for giving them more homework. I wanted to make sure that their inability to immediately answer the question about Thomas's procedure didn't obscure the fact that they did extremely good work in those three hours, so I had a few words to say about that. And the session ended there.

Maxine's Journal

November 20

Looking back on what happened last night, it seems the previous session wasn't just a fluke. Again, all the teachers were working together to figure out the mathematics for themselves and working hard, too, at analyzing student thinking. We are really clicking as a group. I'm not saying that everything is a breeze. There are individuals I'm concerned about and a few points of tension among some of the teachers. And I still have questions about the material and how I can best facilitate this seminar. But on the whole, we're working well together.

Here's an overview of the way Session 6 unfolded: We started out returning to the problem that ended our last session, "What's going on with Thomas's procedure, on the video?" After this discussion, the teachers then moved into small groups for a case discussion, both exploring the mathematics for themselves and looking closely at student thinking in the cases. When we came back together, the whole-group discussion mainly addressed the meaning of division. In preparation for viewing the video, I asked people to solve $159 \div 13$ in their heads, and we talked about the different methods they used. Finally, we viewed the video—a group of fifth graders sharing *their* methods for solving $159 \div 13$—and discussed issues that came up for the teachers as they watched.

Opening discussion: Back to Thomas's procedure

As members of the seminar entered the room, a few mentioned their thoughts on Thomas's procedure for 36×17, and some wanted to show me what they had done. There was enough interest in the group to spend some time talking together about it, so I asked Nadia to start us off.

"When we were working on 16×18 last time, I realized I could see so much more when I set up the problem as an array," Nadia explained. "So when I was thinking about what Thomas had done, I thought I'd be able to figure out what was going on if I looked at an array for that, too. I first made a 36×17 array, and then extended the sides to make a 40×20 array." Instead of trying to draw it on the board, Nadia held up a page that showed her work quite clearly; she had drawn her figure large so that everyone could see it.

Nadia explained what she discovered with this diagram. "See, the problem with what Thomas did is that he added on all this stuff," she pointed to the outer part of the 20×40 array, "but he subtracted off just this 4 and 3." She pointed to the four squares at the top right and the 3 squares at the bottom left.

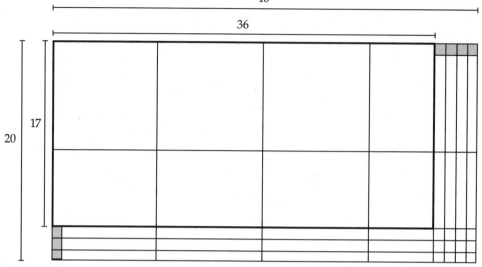

"Ohhhhhhhhh!" That came from Marta, and I asked her what was going on. "I knew he had added on too much, but I couldn't make it come out right. First I thought he needed to subtract off three 36s and four 17s. But that still leaves me with an answer that's 12 too big. Then I thought maybe I needed to take off three 40s and four 20s, but that gave me an answer that's 12 too small. I couldn't figure out what was going on with that 12. But when I look at Nadia's array, there it is!"

I asked Marta what she meant. "After you take away those three 36s and four 17s, you still see those 12 squares in the corner. They have to come off!"

Patsy said she thought about it another way and came to the board to explain. "I thought about Thomas doing the problem in two steps. He started with 36×17. Then he added 4 to 36 to get 40×17. With this step, he added an extra four 17s. And then he changed the problem again—he added 3 to 17 to get 40×20, adding on an extra three 40s. If you subtract 4×17 and 3×40, you get the right answer."

Marta was writing down every word of Patsy's. She said she didn't get it now, but she'd think about it later.

I wasn't sure where the rest of the class was on this, but I didn't want to spend more time on it. Still, these are important ideas. I again wonder if, next time, I can set up Session 5 in a way that will get the teachers into these questions earlier. I was glad that Nadia and Patsy had a chance to show what they had figured out, but it was time for the group to move on to thinking about division.

Small-group case discussion: Base ten blocks and division

I read off who should be in which groups to start the case discussion, and I suggested that they work together to figure out the mathematics that came up in the cases. Almost all the teachers turned first to the base ten blocks and made up problems for themselves, such as $328 \div 2$, $439 \div 3$, and $5636 \div 4$. They

Building a System of Tens

spent a lot of time trying to figure out how this worked. "I start out with 3 hundreds flats, 2 tens rods, and 8 unit cubes that need to get distributed between two groups. First distribute the 3 hundreds flats—each group gets 1, and the third flat gets traded for 10 rods. Now I've got 12 rods to distribute; 6 rods to each group. Then the 8 cubes get distributed. That leaves each group with 1 flat, 6 rods, and 4 cubes, or 164." It took many of the teachers a long time to go through these steps and think through what's going on, and they wanted to do it for several different examples.

While I watched, I wondered whether the time was well spent. I know there are lots of adults who get excited by what they can see with base ten blocks. However, the insights that adults get after many years of work with traditional algorithms aren't necessarily available to elementary school children. Frequently, it seems that children are able to use the base ten blocks to get the right answer without thinking through the underlying ideas. How was this work going to help the teachers with their teaching? But as I watched, I decided to let things go. They were so into what they were doing, and they *were* doing some important thinking for themselves; it would have been inappropriate for me to disrupt it.

In hindsight, I have some other ideas about what I might have done. In fact, I think the decision to let them keep working with the base ten blocks was right. But once we came together for discussion, I could have asked them to think more about their own discoveries and how they are related to what the children were doing when they *weren't* using base ten blocks. For example, if we look at Eleanor's case [case 23, "Discussing Division"] to see how Jen solved $364 \div 2$, she started with $300 \div 2$, but instead of giving each group 100 and trading 100 for 10 tens, she got 150. Then she still had the 64 to divide, and got 32; $150 + 32 = 182$. In what ways were Jen's steps just like what the teachers were doing with base ten blocks? How was Jen's procedure different?

But that's not what we discussed. Once teachers turned to the cases, they worked hard to figure out what the children were doing—but not in comparison to their own new method. They spent a lot of time with Janie's case "Sharing Jelly Beans" [case 24], acting out the jelly bean problems: 134 jelly beans shared among 6 kids, and then 143 jelly beans shared among 8 kids. Then they worked on Andy's method for solving $453 \div 6$.

Whole-group discussion: What division means

Even though everyone was engaged in exploring division, I was concerned that some primary-grade teachers in the group felt this work didn't relate to their teaching. I heard some comments like, "This is fun and interesting, but I don't do this kind of mathematics in my grade." Because of this sentiment, I asked the group to think about the various ideas involved in solving problems like these. Which of those ideas are appropriate for young children to begin thinking about? That is, if you want your students to be able to do work like this when they are older, what should they be working on now?

As the teachers got into this, they left behind the large numbers and considerations of how they can be decomposed to perform the operation, and began thinking about what division *means.* All of them felt that, no matter what grade they taught, their students should be able to think about what happens if you have a certain amount of something and you have to share it equally.

As we got into this, we spent a long time talking about 36 ÷ 3. Patsy said that 36 ÷ 3 means 3 groups of 12: You take away 12 and then another 12 and then another 12. Claire said that if you think about it that way, you already have to know the answer to do the division. Wasn't Patsy's problem actually 36 ÷ 12? To sort this out, I suggested that the class come up with a problem context to work with.

Nadia suggested this: Share 36 cookies among 3 children. First, you give each child 1, that's 3 cookies; then another, that's 6 cookies; and you keep going around until all the cookies have been given out. Each child gets 12 cookies.

Marjorie said, "What if you have 36 candies in bags of 3?" In the silence that followed, Marta said, almost under her breath, "Wow!" When I asked her what kind of wow that was, she replied, "I've just never thought about this before; 36 ÷ 3 was just a thing to me. It never occurred to me that there could be more than one way to think about it."

At this point several teachers joined in, saying they had never thought about how situations helped to make sense of the operations. It was interesting to me that this issue was coming up now, since it is actually the theme of our second-semester seminar (Number and Operations, Part 2: *Making Meaning for Operations*): looking at the operations as models of situations and using situations to learn about the operations. In fact, throughout *Building a System of Tens,* the children *are* using their understandings of problem contexts, as in Lynn's case [case 17], when Fiona needed to think about whether the birds stayed or flew away in order to know whether to add or subtract, or in Janie's case [case 24], when the children use the idea of sharing jelly beans to figure out how to divide. However, our attention has been mainly on how children understand the base ten structure of numbers and how they use that understanding to maneuver around the number system. It feels fine to me that the group is beginning to pose questions that we'll be pursuing more deeply next semester.

Toward the end of this discussion, Patsy said, "Well, this totally changes everything." I asked her what she meant. "Well, if I only give the same problem all the time . . . I never even thought of that. They need to see division both ways!"

Mental warm-ups before the video

In the video we were about to watch, students from a fifth-grade class show their ways of solving $159 \div 13$. But before asking the teachers to follow the fifth graders' thinking, I thought it would be good for them to think about the numbers for themselves. Besides, the mental computation has been good for them. The teachers are developing much greater flexibility with the numbers, and they recognize that they are getting better at it each time they do it.

Marta offered her method first: "$159 = 130 + 29$; 130 is ten 13s and 29 is two 13s with 3 left over. So, 12 remainder 3."

Patsy said that her way was similar, but she broke up 159 into 104 and 55. "$104 \div 13 = 8$ and $55 \div 13 = 4$ r 3. Therefore, 12 remainder 3." Everyone listened and then there was a pause until someone finally said, "Yeah, it works. But why did you come up with 104 and 55?" Patsy explained that she has played cards a lot. "There are 52 cards in a deck, 4 suits of 13 cards each. So I know that $13 \times 4 = 52$. Double that and I get $13 \times 8 = 104$." She said that it was easy to think about dividing by 13 when she thought about cards.

At this point Velma said she wanted to show her way of solving the problem even though she knew it didn't make sense. She was laughing as she went to the board and said, "I did it the way we've been solving problems all semester. I said that 159 is $150 + 9$ and 13 is $10 + 3$. So I divided each part: $150 \div 10 = 15$; $9 \div 3 = 3$. Then, look, $15 - 3 = 12$ and that's the answer."

Well, yes, Velma's way was similar to all those ways the children took apart numbers and put them together when they were adding and subtracting. But here we are dividing, and so we were back to the discussion about what division means. Does Velma's approach make sense of what it means to divide?

Claire offered: "We have to think about groups of things. How many groups of 13 can you get from 159? If you look at what Velma did, she said you have 15 groups of 10 and 3 groups of 3. That doesn't help you think about groups of 13. It's just a coincidence that you can subtract the numbers and come up with the right answer."

Marjorie suggested we try Velma's way with other numbers. "What if you had $258 \div 11$?" Marjorie went to the board to write down the equivalent steps: $250 \div 10 = 25$; $8 \div 1 = 8$; $25 - 8 = 17$. "So what's $258 \div 11$?"

At first people didn't have a way to assess whether the answer might actually be 17. Finally, they realized they could use any of their other methods. Velma said you can think about 258 as $220 + 38$. "You get 20 groups of 11 from 220 and 3 groups of 11 from 38 with 5 left over. So the answer is 23 remainder 5."

At this point, I started the video.

Viewing and discussing the video

As I've mentioned before, the work we have been doing with the print cases has been important in giving the teachers a strong sense of the variety of ways children think about arithmetic. Having the methods in writing, the teachers can spend time thinking through the logic of what the children did. In this way, they have the opportunity to learn the mathematics for themselves. Now, watching the video, the teachers could follow the children's methods as they spoke. That is, they could practice listening to students the way they might in their own classes.

For this video segment, as I have done before, I showed one or two children's procedures at a time, stopping in between to discuss what we had just seen.

Claire offered a recap of what Elaine had done for $159 \div 13$. "She took $13 \times 10 = 130$, and then added on another two 13s, and that's all that fits in 159."

Patsy added, "When she totaled up her twelve 13s to 156, at first she was confused about what her answer was. But when the teacher asked, she was clear that it was 12 remainder 3."

The group was confused about what Yuriy was up to—why start with 13×13? Sheila commented, "Oh, he's just showing off all the facts he knows. He probably has them memorized up to 20×20."

Marjorie considered, "Maybe he knows his squares. Maybe that's an easy fact for him."

Helen added, "He did say you'd take a number you would know. I think it's what Marjorie said. He doesn't get it that other people don't have in their heads what 13×13 is."

None of the teachers mentioned that, as Yuriy said the correct answer, "12 remainder 3," he wrote 12.3 on the board. On the video, the teacher posed questions to clarify what he intended, 12 groups of 13 with 3 left over, and chose not to draw attention to the notational error. I had expected that the teacher's decision to handle it this way would cause a certain amount of turmoil among seminar participants, but it didn't. When I asked about it, people accepted the teacher's response as an appropriate pedagogical decision. The teacher was focusing the class on another set of issues; she would be able to work with the class on the meaning of decimals later.

When we saw Thomas on the video, the group recognized him from the previous video segment on multiplication. People listened intently as he explained his procedure and cheered when he gave the correct answer.

We spent some time talking about what Shannon had done, especially since it resembled Velma's procedure in our own mental math exercise. However, instead of splitting 159 into 150 and 9 the way Velma did, Shannon split it into 100 and 59. And instead of splitting the 13 into 10 and 3, Shannon knew that she needed to find how many 13s in each part, 100 and 59. Because of our discussion earlier in the session, the group seemed to be able to sort that out.

After viewing Alosha, Nadia pointed out that he gave a definition of division different from any that our group had talked about. He said division was "counting by something and knowing how many times you count." Nadia said that in her class, students practice skip counting all the time—they count by twos, threes, fives, tens. But she never asks them anything like, "If you count to 10 by twos, how many numbers do you say on the way?" This was something she wanted to start doing.

At the end of the video, we saw Carla solve the problem by drawing 159 circles and putting them into groups of 13, and then we watched Kevin apply the familiar long division algorithm, though he couldn't explain the logic behind what he had done. Now our seminar discussion turned to the balance between understanding and efficiency. Even though the whole group agreed that Carla's method is extremely cumbersome, some argued for the power of knowing that she can get the right answer and knowing why her method works. Some teachers remarked that when they balance their own check-books, they sometimes make dots to help them count the numbers; or, even if they use a calculator, they do it again by hand just to be sure it's right. So they thought this was what some of the children were doing—even if you know more sophisticated and supposedly more efficient ways, there are times when you might choose to use a lengthier method.

This discussion, which was essentially about the role of the conventional algorithm, was quite different from the one that took place in Session 4 after watching the video about addition and subtraction strategies. This time it seemed that the teachers weren't so sure that speed and efficiency necessarily connect with the traditional algorithm. It wasn't as if they were saying that they'd be satisfied if their students knew a laborious method, such as drawing out circles and slash marks, and nothing else. But they are seeing that you *can* have speed and efficiency with many different procedures, not just the one they've always taught.

This took us to the end of the session. The discussions were all quite rich and satisfying. As always, however, I do have questions about what is going on with the quiet people. To what extent are they thinking through the logic of the children's procedures? Are they working as much on the ideas as the vocal people are?

In particular, I'm curious about whether everyone in the group recognized Yuriy's error. Do they realize that 12.3 does not mean 12 remainder 3? Maybe it was only a few vocal participants who realized there was an error in notation. In the same way the teacher in the videotape held this question for later, I will need to follow up this issue in our next session, when we work on decimals.

Maxine's Journal

December 4

As I prepared for this session, I was thinking about how this would be the last case discussion from the *Building a System of Tens* casebook. At the same time, it would be our first venture into the realm of rational numbers. So, at the very same time we would be approaching some kind of resting place, we'd also be opening up a new can of worms! What *are* the implications of that?

As I wrote, I paused at the phrase "some kind of resting place." I almost wrote "closure" and then decided that simply wasn't it. I guess this marks yet another difference from the way schooling has been in past decades. Achieving closure is not a goal. It's appropriate for teachers and students to leave each class—even when it's near the end of the semester—with still more questions. That's the nature of inquiry: Each answer yields more questions.

However, I do believe it's important to take time periodically to look back over past lessons, to reflect, and to think about issues emerging from the whole. That's one reason for the homework assignment to review the cases we have read this semester. And the group will continue with this reflection for our next session, because I expect that reading "Highlights of Related Research" will help the teachers look at the casebook as a whole.

Anyway, this was the Session 7 agenda: (1) discussion of the homework, looking at cases from the whole semester to say which were particularly interesting or effective and why; (2) a math activity to design visual representations of decimal amounts; and (3) small-group and whole-group case discussion.

Homework discussion: Picking a favorite case

The teachers seemed to enjoy reviewing the cases and thinking about them in relation to their own teaching over the last few months. Shannon wrote that being asked to pick just one was "like asking me to pick only one jelly bean from 27 luscious varieties of Jelly Belly jelly beans. It's kind of impossible." But she did choose, as did everyone else.

It was striking to me that, except for three teachers who chose the first case, no two teachers picked the same one. I think the three who chose Ann's case ["Do My Students Think Flexibly? Do I?"] were struck by their first realization that children can have their own ways of doing the mathematics they are being taught. When I listened carefully to the teachers' explanations of their choices, I began to notice that the reasons fell into three categories. Now, after class, as I look over what they wrote, I still see those categories.

Some teachers, like those who picked Ann's case, explained that it taught them something important about children's thinking. Velma wrote, "I was intrigued that a teacher would ask *how* the children had arrived at the answer to a two-digit addition example. I was amazed that not every student solved the example in the traditional way, and I was floored that they could get the correct answer without starting in the ones column. This piece, coupled with our class discussion, had me wondering. Did my third graders approach their math with the same flexibility these sixth graders showed?"

Others chose a case that stimulated new insights about mathematics. For example, Shannon identified the readings about division. (In the end, she couldn't pick a single case and instead picked a chapter of the casebook.) She explained that this set of cases helped her see how division is related to subtraction. She wrote, "As simple as it sounds, that one interaction [while working from those cases] really made an impact on me, as multiplication and division were just something I did by a rote method, with not much thought as to how addition, subtraction, multiplication, and division are all related."

The third category was more closely tied to teaching. For example, Patsy identified one of the multiplication cases as the one that had the greatest impact. "The reason was that it caused a great deal of discussion for me about how I teach multiplication." She said that Susannah's case, "Multiplication Revisited" [case 21], made her realize that though she was comfortable with the way she taught multiplication, it wasn't necessarily the way her students saw things. "I was forced into relooking and reevaluating what was comfortable for me."

Claire wrote about "Why Do We Need Rules?" by Nicole: "This narrative acted as a reminder to me that my understanding of how to teach mathematics is in process, just as is my students' learning. When I find my class struggling to make sense of something new, I need to remember that it is a natural part of the process. And, I need to help *them* see it as natural, too."

After the teachers talked about their favorite cases, I mentioned that they were going to be writing cases of their own, and their first one would be due at our next meeting. In contrast to the dread I had anticipated, they seemed quite responsive to this assignment. "Oh, goody!" is what Marta said.

Even though those who were vocal didn't seem intimidated by the assignment, I still pointed out that the cases they have been reading were not teachers' first attempts; nor were they first drafts of later attempts. Rather, these cases were written by teachers who had both practice doing it and opportunities to edit after sharing their cases with colleagues. I wanted my group to know that, if their first attempts didn't look the same, they shouldn't be embarrassed to bring them in. Even if it seemed hard, I wanted everyone to bring in something, and then we would talk about what they learned from doing it. I'm curious about what they'll be bringing in.

Math activity: Representing decimal numbers

I started the math activity by talking about what we saw in the video last week—a child solving 159 ÷ 13, getting 12 with 3 left over, but recording it as

12.3, showing the remainder as a decimal. What did the group think about that? Patsy spoke up first: "I think the boy didn't remember what decimals are. He might have misremembered the rule that when you have a remainder, you can write it as a fraction. None of the kids wrote their answer as $12\frac{3}{13}$, but that would be correct. Maybe he was thinking about that, but got it wrong and wrote 12.3 instead."

I asked, "So what's the difference between $12\frac{3}{13}$ and 12.3?"

Patsy looked surprised, but answered the question: "12.3 means 12 and 3 tenths, not 12 and 3 thirteenths."

I didn't know what to do next. The issue was out in the open, but all I learned was that Patsy knew something about decimal notation. I still didn't know about others in the group, particularly some of the quiet folks.

Then I handed out and explained the math activity: to devise at least two ways to represent given decimal numbers. People got up to select materials and then settled into the task.

Sitting down with Nadia and Marjorie, I posed some questions about what they had represented with the blocks—2 rods and 5 cubes—and they told me "that's point twenty-five." There certainly didn't seem anything wrong to me, but suddenly Marjorie started laughing. "You know, we're treating it as if it were just 25! We never paid attention to what 1 should be!" I asked Nadia if she knew what Marjorie was talking about, and she shook her head.

"Look," Marjorie said. "We usually think of the small cube as the unit; each cube is 1. So if we have 2 rods and 5 cubes, it's 25—not .25 [twenty-five hundredths]. But if we say, OK, the flat now stands for 1. The rod is 1 tenth of that and the cube is 1 hundredth of that. That's the difference."

It seemed to me that Nadia was going to need some time to understand the point Marjorie was making. But as I visited other groups, the same issue appeared to be coming up.

Claire and her partner had joined another group, and she was talking about how confusing it must be for children. "All these years the materials have been associated with ones, tens, and hundreds, and suddenly they have to mean something else." She held up a small cube: "For years this has been 1, and now it isn't anymore! Doesn't that confuse children?"

I wasn't sure about whether I should say out loud what I was thinking, but decided to go ahead: "I saw some evidence of that right here—with adults."

Helen giggled. Then Carla spoke up, "When we first started using them, it was hard." She held up a rod, "I mean, is this a 1?" and then, holding up a flat, "Or this?"

Helen said, "It was odd at first, but then it got more familiar, and it's cool. Developing that flexibility. It takes experience, and then you get it and think, 'Oh, yeah, I could trade.'"

I liked this exchange because it was clear that Helen and Carla were talking about their own experiences and what they were learning about using the blocks. It's not that the mathematics is in the blocks; the mathematics is in your head. If you're using blocks to represent the mathematics, there's a process to go through as you learn to make the representation work for you. Just following someone else's model isn't enough.

When we came together to discuss what the small groups had been working on, several teachers shared the representations they were using to think about decimals. We went back to the issue of what is 1 and then on to the difference between 15 *hundreds* and 15 *hundredths.*

Another interesting question came up about the representations people were using: What does it mean to trade 1 of something for 10 of something? Does it have to look 10 bigger, or can't you just remember 1 of these is worth 10 of these? In fact, if you used pennies and dimes, the dime isn't ten times as big as a penny, but you know the dime is 1 tenth of a dollar and the penny is 1 hundredth. Some of the teachers use chip-trading, with chips the same size but of different colors for different values.

Sheila and Tomi's representation got everyone thinking about this. To represent .33, these two teachers put 3 unit cubes on top of a rod (3 tenths) and 3 unit cubes on top of a flat (3 hundredths). According to them, these showed 3 over 10 and 3 over 100, respectively, and together: .3 + .03 = .33. Sheila and Tomi were confident of their scheme and weren't bothered when others pointed out that it didn't show quantity correctly.

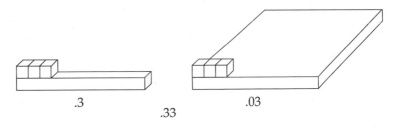

I have my own questions as I think back to Lucy's case, "Keeping It Straight" [case 6]. There, Sarah was working with whole numbers—black cubes representing ones; yellow cubes, tens. Since the different values of the cubes weren't represented by their size, Sarah needed to do some hard thinking to figure out how her representation would work for sums that involved regrouping. What would have happened if I had asked Sheila and Tomi to demonstrate .38 + .45 using their representation? Would they have felt so confident? Would they have been able to work the ideas through as Sarah had—and as they themselves actually had when they worked on Lucy's case? I hadn't been thinking quickly enough during the session to give them a problem that involves regrouping. This is another item I'll make note of next time I teach the seminar.

Group discussion of the cases

Once small groups began to address the cases, it became clear that the work they had just done really helped them think about what was going on with the students who are portrayed. Most of their time was dedicated first to

Steven in Henrietta's case, "Tenths and Hundredths" [case 25], and then to Nicole's March case, "When the Answer *Is* Important" [case 28].

When we came together as a whole group, we shared lists that the teachers had made about Steven's ideas—list of the things he "gets" and the things he is missing. They pointed out that Steven could name every place and number correctly as long as they were individual digits. Someone said that he knew to add the same things together. That is, 2 tenths and 5 hundredths (.25) added to 6 tenths (.6) is 8 tenths and 5 hundredths (.85). Someone suggested that he "knew the 1 to 10 relationship," but several teachers disagreed. They now know to ask, "Where in the case do you see evidence of that?" In the end, the teachers seemed to agree that the case presents no evidence of whether Steven understood this or not. Rather, this point would go in a third list—the list of what we don't know about Steven's understanding.

I asked in what way this work with decimals resembled work with whole numbers and in what way it differed. Carla referred to how Steven came up with .515 when he added .28 and .37. She said that it seemed like the same error children make who get 515 while adding 28 and 37; the confusion isn't just over decimals. "It has to do with the fact that we can't put a two-digit number in a one-digit slot."

At this point Velma, who had seemed exasperated in her small group, declared, "Just by adding that point, you forget everything you knew and you're starting at zero again. You feel that way, anyway. Decimal numbers are completely different from whole numbers!"

I asked, "Are you saying these decimals feel like completely new territory?"

"Yes!" Velma lamented. "All those rules we knew. Will they work or what? It feels like starting all over again."

In fact, Velma was right. It's not that you forget everything, but many of the generalizations for whole numbers don't apply to rationals. To sort out what works and what doesn't, everything has to be thrown into question. For example, reading Nicole's January case, "Why Do We Need Rules?" the group found that some rules for comparing whole numbers don't apply to decimals.

My question to myself is, Does this have to be exasperating? If it's understood that each time you expand the domain you're working on, you need to investigate which generalizations still apply and which need to be refined or revised, then maybe the emotion can be excitement instead of exasperation. In the seminar for Number and Operations, Part 2, we're going to look at this question when we talk about operating with fractions.

But for now, I suggested that we think about addition of decimals. "In what ways are adding whole numbers and adding decimals the same, and in what ways are they different?"

People at first posited many differences, but by the end of the discussion, came to see none! For example, the first thing someone stated as a difference was that we line up whole numbers from right to left, whereas we line decimals up from the decimal point. Patsy suggested that if you have two decimals with the same number of places, you also line them up from the right. "Wait a minute," Marjorie declared. "The kids in Nicole's class sorted that out. You line up tenths with tenths and hundredths with hundredths. No matter what kind of numbers you're dealing with, you line up like places with like places." So, the group agreed, this is a similarity, not a difference.

I was quite taken aback when Tammy suggested that when we add decimals, the quantities get smaller, but when we add whole numbers, the quantities get bigger. People actually thought about this for a moment. I suggested we look back at the decimals we had just been adding.

Helen said, "No way! Like in Nicole's class again, the problem was about adding up these small amounts of gold. When you put those amounts together, you end up with more."

Everyone then stated that no, in fact, even decimal addition makes numbers bigger. Patsy stated authoritatively that when we multiply, the result ends up being smaller. I noticed some panicked expressions at the mention of multiplying decimals, so I said that multiplying decimals and fractions would be something we'd be looking at in greater depth in Part 2, but not right now.

The third difference was proposed by Helen, who said that the places got smaller as you go to the right of the decimal and larger as you go to the left. I asked her to come up and show us what she meant and she approached the board, pulled up sharply, and said, "Oops, never mind!"

"What did you just figure out?" I asked.

"It doesn't matter where you're looking," she explained. "The places always get smaller as you go to the right, and larger as you go to the left—that's not a difference."

Now Velma started getting antsy again. "So, I don't get it! You mean there aren't any differences?"

I said that it's not quite true that there are no differences, but the differences get us to rethink the rules. Take, for example, the rule for lining up numbers to add. There's a logic behind the way we do it, and the logic is the same for both whole numbers and decimals. But if we don't think about the logic, and just look at how the numbers are placed, it appears that there are two different rules: For whole numbers, we line them up at the right; for decimals, we line up the decimal point.

"The thing is," I said, "when you're working only with whole numbers, you just do it. You don't even think about why you do it that way. It's when you start working with decimals and you have to do something that *seems* different—then you start thinking about *why*. Thinking about what's going on when you add decimals gets you to see things about adding whole numbers that we never think about because we take them for granted. That's what I like about this stuff."

That was more of a lecture than I usual get myself into. I don't really know what its impact was. Since it was 7:00 by now, our discussion ended there.

"I think we all have a lot to think about," I said to mark the end of class. "Enjoy writing your cases! And the reading assignment is different from usual. I hope you like that, too."

Maxine's Journal

December 18

At the end of the *Building a System of Tens* seminar, it's now my turn to reflect over the last several months. But before I do that, I should report on the events of our last session. We spent most of our time in two activities: small-group sharing of the cases the teachers wrote, taken from their own classes, and whole-group discussion of the essay "Highlights of Related Research."

Sharing the teachers' cases

As we gathered for this session, I could sense a lot of excitement about the cases the group had written. In previous sessions, they had brought material from their own classrooms—for the first session, samples of their students' work, and midway through the semester, the results of their math interview—but this was different. At this stage of the seminar, the work they bring in reflects new learnings. They are excited about what is happening in their classrooms and are eager to share with their colleagues. Just as important, perhaps, they are now writing in the genre of the material they have been studying. Having at last produced cases like those in the casebook, they find that their relationship to the material shifts. This is my conjecture: They are coming to see the authors of the cases in the casebook as *peers*. The authors are teachers, just as they are, and the children they read about are much like their own.

I put people in groups of three; groups this small would have time to read each other's cases and still have plenty of time for discussion. I suggested they read all three cases before starting to talk and then address two questions: What similarities do you see across episodes? What is unique to each one? I also pointed out that they needed to pay attention to the time, so each case could be discussed.

Although I was curious, I decided not to listen in on the small-group discussions. I knew that their ownership was important here, and my presence might detract from that. I wanted them to be able to share their work without wondering what I might be thinking. And so while they met, I took notes about my own reflections on the semester.

Discussion of the research essay

I was aware that the essay "Highlights of Related Research" had a lot in it for the teachers to digest, and I thought long and hard about how we might best approach this material as a group. In the end, I decided to use a "jigsaw" strategy. First I put the teachers into five groups and assigned one section of the essay, or one of its themes, to each group. They would spend time together discussing that theme, exploring questions that it brought up for them, and considering how the points in that section of the essay illuminate specific cases or events from their own classrooms. After 20 minutes, they would form new groups, each with at least one representative from each of the original five groups. In this new configuration they would go through the entire essay, section by section, with the representative of each section leading the group in a discussion of that theme for five minutes.

As I moved from group to group, I saw that the teachers were quite engaged. Some groups stayed pretty close to the text of the essay, others strayed, but all were involved in serious thinking.

When I observed the group discussing the first section, "Written Number vs. Spoken Number," they were looking carefully at the text. These teachers had come a long way since we first discussed those ideas in our third session—back then, it was new to them to be thinking about children's logic. By now, the ideas had settled and they could consider them with a greater sense of solidity. They seemed to enjoy going back to those cases to consider from their new perspective what the children were saying.

In the next group, where the theme was "Seeing a Ten as 'One,'" the teachers talked about the fact that children might get right answers to various questions and still not have a solid sense of place value. Sheila made the point that a child might use the terms *tens place* and *ones place* "without really knowing what those terms mean." In response, Helen said that she now felt confused about how to think about her students' understandings. As she has begun listening to her students in a new way over the last few months, she has noticed that one day a child apparently "gets it," yet the next day that same child seems very confused.

At this point, I asked, "What does it mean to 'get it'?" Then there was silence, but not an uncomfortable silence—the teachers were thinking hard.

When Carla asked, tentatively, "What if they never get it? Can that happen?" the others in the group blurted out that *they* were just getting it! Although nobody ventured to say what "getting it" means, there was an implicit assumption that "getting it" isn't an on-or-off thing. They began to talk about the importance of assessing progress rather than only mastery.

Sheila continued the conversation, asking, "Is place value a thing to do?" Helen said that she was using a unit on place value by Marilyn Burns and, even though it was a well-defined unit, her class had been working on it all year and was still not finished.

Maybe I should have asked Helen to explain, because I'm not sure what she meant. But Carla spoke up and asked, "Isn't it important that kids can do 1004 – 138 and say 100 tens becomes 99 tens?" The others nodded, and it was quiet for a moment. I still don't know just what Carla meant. What does she think a child who can say "100 tens becomes 99 tens" understands?

In another small group, Marjorie said that she should have been in the group discussing Ross's experiments. She explained that she simply didn't believe the results of those experiments, and so she tried out the same questions with her own students. After I listened to what Marjorie had done, I said that I'd like her to repeat her story when we gathered again as a whole group.

Then she and her partners got back into their discussion of the third section, "Invented Procedures for Adding and Subtracting." Tammy brought up what was happening in her third-grade class. She said she had been having her students solve problems with manipulatives, and they did very well. However, when she gave them a paper-and-pencil test on the same content, they couldn't do the work. She was surprised and disappointed. Claire commented that solving problems with manipulatives and solving the same kind of problems with paper and pencil are different experiences for children. She said that the mathematical ideas are the same to Tammy, but not necessarily to the children.

Those who were discussing the fourth section, "Invented Procedures for Multiplying and Dividing," mainly spent their time working through the mathematical issues for themselves, particularly to clarify what is meant by distributivity.

When I got around to the group discussing the fifth section, "Understanding Decimal Fractions," they were poring over the part that refers to Nicole's March case [case 28], in which fifth graders try to add fractional grams of gold as decimal numbers. The teachers in this group were still mulling over the ideas they had been working on during the previous session, talking about how surprising it was to discover that the rules for adding decimals are really the same as the rules for adding whole numbers.

When the groups were reconfigured with at least one representative for each section, everyone was very serious about her responsibility to report on the points that came up in her first group's discussion. As a result, everyone got a good overview of the essay.

Calling the whole group together, I first asked Marjorie to tell her story. As she had told me, she explained to the group that she simply didn't believe the results of Ross's experiments as described in the essay and so, as a test, had put her students into pairs and posed the same questions to them, one pair at a time. "I tried it with ordinary kids, and no one did what those children did."

Joan looked dubious. "Just because your students didn't do the same thing doesn't mean that we should dismiss what Ross reported. Maybe there's still something about children's understanding of place value that we need to think about."

I suggested that we look back at that part of the essay. Tammy summarized for us, "Ross gave them 25 sticks, and the children could count and say it was 25. When she asked what the 5 in 25 means, they could say. But when she asked what the 2 means, not even half the children could tell her what the 2 represented in terms of the sticks."

Velma said, "Yeah, they understand 25, the quantity. But they don't understand what it is made up of."

Marta asked, "What do we learn when children do the problems right, and what do we learn when they do them wrong? What does any of that tell us about what they understand or what they have learned?"

I added, "And what does it help us understand about the mathematics to be learned?"

Thinking about the relationship of these teachers to educational research, I found this last discussion rather interesting. I was impressed that Marjorie would challenge something she read by testing it on her own students. And the questions Joan and Marta asked were good ones. It's not just a matter of reading what the researchers report, but trying to figure out the implications. What do the findings mean for their work with their own students?

I asked if there were other points anyone wanted to make about the essay. Claire said that she agreed with the text, that understanding place value is not a prerequisite for understanding multidigit computation—students can work on these ideas together. This induced several teachers to make disparaging comments about textbooks that teach by little steps and separate place value, addition without regrouping, subtraction without regrouping, addition with regrouping, subtraction with regrouping, and so on, instead of having all of this integrated. As this was being said, I checked facial expressions, because I think this describes the way some teachers in the group still teach. I was wondering if anyone would object and was concerned that some of them might be feeling anxious. However, from the reactions I saw, the teachers who probably work this way seemed to agree with what was being said. *They* wouldn't characterize their teaching as not being integrated, even if I would. Anyway, these remarks didn't seem to distress anyone.

Patsy asked, "Do we ever have to teach them the algorithm? I mean, what if they can do the problems their own way? Do they ever need to know how to do the algorithm?" Nobody suggested an answer here. Still more questions arose: What about using calculators? When is it important to know facts *fast?*

There does seem to be consensus on the importance of knowing facts. Thinking back on the cases they read this last semester, they saw that the children who were coming up with their own methods of calculation seemed to be quite solid with their basic facts. It's empowering and useful to know them, the teachers agreed. However, instead of giving timed tests and applying pressure, they now wanted to provide a "friendly" setting to encourage their students to learn their math facts.

The teachers had strayed from the essay itself, now discussing the pedagogical questions that loomed largest for them. This was important and useful at the end of the semester, but I still had one more question about the essay for them: "What was it like for you to read this research after studying all those cases?"

Marta responded, "It felt like a confirmation of everything I had been thinking."

That took me by surprise, and so I asked her what she meant. She said, "Throughout the fall, as we read the cases, I was coming to my own conclusions about children's thinking. It felt good to know that all those researchers came to the same conclusions. It confirms what I was already thinking."

Others in the group were nodding. I asked Marjorie what she thought about that, and she shrugged.

Closing with mental math

At this point I was aware that we were close to the end of the session, and we weren't going to be meeting again (for Part 2 of the DMI seminar) for several weeks. I wanted to do something to mark the end of the semester and to reflect the progress they had made. And so I told them that, to celebrate, we were going to do some mental math. They laughed, but seemed enthusiastic once we started with $347 + 260$, $204 - 189$, 31×16, and $245 \div 11$. In fact, they felt fluent and were proud of the ways they could think about the calculations.

Further reflections

Now that we've finished the *Building a System of Tens* seminar, I have a lot to think about. How do things stand since we started last September? I've reread my journal, and here are my thoughts.

Looking over what I wrote in my pre-seminar entry, before I met the group, I feel that I still hold those same goals—and that we have made progress toward them. The teachers are developing a different sense of mathematics, are learning about themselves as mathematical thinkers, and are becoming stronger mathematical thinkers.

From changes I've seen in the way the teachers read and interact with the cases, I believe that they are all coming to recognize that children can be mathematical thinkers. However, looking at the interviews they conducted midway through the seminar and the cases they wrote at the end, I'm not so confident that they all think of their own students as mathematical thinkers. Some teachers do, but not all. And even if they have an inkling that their students might be able to think mathematically *if given opportunities,* they aren't so sure they want to create those opportunities in their classrooms.

Similarly, I believe most of the teachers are learning how to analyze children's mathematical thinking. However, I'm not sure how much of this carries over to their teaching. Do they work hard to figure out what their own students are thinking, in what ways their students' ideas make sense, where their students might be confused? Some do, but not all.

My fourth goal was to have the teachers learn to involve the whole class in the analysis of an individual student's ideas. Now I wonder if this is just too big a leap for most of the teachers in this group. I think I've seen beginnings in some of our discussions. For example, in Session 5, when the group talked about the power of Jen's method of solution and the triviality of her addition error, they thought about how student interactions could lead Jen to recognize her mistake and, at the same time, acknowledge the strength of her thinking.

Many of the cases in the casebook illustrate children thinking about mathematical ideas together. The group does have images of this. However, it is difficult to facilitate a mathematics discussion in which ideas from different students connect and build. To be sure, in order to do this, teachers need to have made some progress toward my other goals—recognizing that mathematics is about ideas, knowing oneself as a mathematical thinker, knowing one's students as mathematical thinkers, and being able to analyze children's mathematical ideas. Let me feel satisfied with that for now.

Finally, I wanted the group to develop a stance of communal inquiry—to learn how to pose their own questions, formulate conjectures, and use discussion with colleagues to move ideas forward. Certainly, we have made considerable progress there, but as I reread my journal, I began to feel somewhat uneasy on this score.

Everything I've described in my journal actually happened, and there clearly was a dramatic shift in the group from Session 4 to Session 5. But I realize that, in my relief that things began to go much better in Session 5, I stopped writing about my concerns. I wrote, "Not everything is perfect," but then recorded all the interesting things that were said. So, here are some of my concerns.

Back in Session 1, I wrote about how important it is *not* to feel that it is up to me to fill silences. But sometimes those silences seem to go on forever! Yes, in each session, important and interesting things are said. But how many times have I asked a question or made a comment that just falls into dead air? I don't get it! Is it that they don't really like holding whole-group discussions? But how can I say that? I look back over this journal and see such interesting insights! I really don't know what to make of this.

Also, rereading my journal, I realize that some teachers' names are rarely mentioned. Now, there are those who are quiet, but there isn't anyone who has never spoken. So why are they absent in my record? I think it is because, quite frankly, they're not engaging in the ideas of the seminar.

For example, whenever Vivian speaks, she makes an analogy to language or says something about children misinterpreting words. She tends to say things like, "First we tell children to write *on* the line when we mean *between* the lines, and then in music they are to put notes *on* the line. That must be confusing." Another time she pointed out that we tell students to put their names at the "top of the paper," but the top of the paper is the whole surface that is facing up. There isn't anything wrong with these points in themselves, but her comments never get at a mathematical idea. It's as if she feels the need to say something and so she looks for some comment she can make that *appears* connected—but to me it always seems beside the point.

It's not as if I record only those comments I agree with. For example, I write about Shannon even though, or because, I'm disturbed by what she says—as when she declared, "My students are so uncreative." Still, what Shannon says *is* to the point, even though sometimes I wish she would say something else. And what she says does offer me something to think about and respond to.

So if there are teachers, like Vivian, who aren't getting to the heart of the matter, what can I do to help them learn? What is my responsibility? Is it sufficient that I provide a context in which learning is possible if they would take a step into it? What can I do to bring Vivian in?

I have a different concern about Patsy. She is clearly very sharp and likes to be recognized as someone who knows. How much is she letting in? Is she allowing herself to be challenged? Is she so concerned about already knowing that she can't let herself learn?

Sometimes I find Patsy's tone of authority annoying—and it's all the more disturbing that many teachers in the group then look to her as an authority. Early on in the seminar, they realized that I wasn't going to provide answers or tell them what to do, and so they are happy to turn to Patsy to get their answers. And Patsy's happy to give them. What I worry about, then, is that those teachers aren't given enough space to find their own ideas.

That last sentence just helped me become clearer about the logic of my own pedagogical stance. When I don't answer questions and don't tell people what to do, it's not that I choose to be withholding. Nor is it that I don't like to talk about my ideas. I do! However, when I am teaching, the priority is for my students (in this case, the teachers) to discover their own ideas first and, from there, to develop them or challenge them or change them. Because of what the teachers expect from *their* teacher when they begin a seminar with me, if my voice is too loud, they won't find their own. As their voices become stronger, my voice can join in.

My fear is that Patsy's voice is suppressing some of the other voices in the group. It's not that she is doing this intentionally, but it is a consequence of what she's doing. For example, Shannon is so timid, but she does have ideas and I want them to be heard—especially by herself. And so whenever I make up small groups, I deliberately put Shannon and Patsy in separate groups. I also keep Sheila and Tomi away from her—and, yes, Vivian, too.

So at the end of Number and Operations, Part 1: *Building a System of Tens*, how do I conclude my journal? I want to weigh the progress we have made and the concerns I have. We've come very far since we first gathered in September. We also have a ways to go. Fortunately, we have another eight sessions together as we work through Number and Operations, Part 2: *Making Meaning for Operations.* That means I have another eight sessions to help *all* the teachers find their voices and express their ideas.

Note: "Maxine's Journal" continues in the facilitator's guide for the DMI seminar on Number and Operations, Part 2: *Making Meaning for Operations.*

Two Portraits of Change

Introduction

While "Maxine's Journal" offers a panoramic view of a DMI seminar, describing the experiences of a group of 18 teachers working through the seminar materials, this essay narrows the field of focus. Here, the facilitator we know as Maxine tracks the specific progress of two of those teachers through the DMI pilot seminars on Number and Operations—Part 1, *Building a System of Tens*, and Part 2, *Making Meaning for Operations*. The set of portfolio assignments from those two seminars, which gave the participants a forum for reflection, also gave the facilitator considerable insight into the experiences of individual participants.

In the following essay, Maxine details the journeys of Shannon, a fourth-grade teacher, and Claire, a first-grade teacher, through the first seminar. Maxine includes excerpts from their written responses to the portfolio assignments, interspersed with her reflections on their work. Note that the DMI materials have undergone some revision since the pilot seminars were held; thus the assignments referred to in the text do not exactly correspond to the ones suggested in the current set of materials.

Shannon: A "very traditional" teacher

The first night of the seminar, Shannon pulled me aside to confide that both her own teaching and her school system were "very traditional." The following day, I examined the samples of student work she had brought in as part of the first assignment, "Collect and analyze work samples from three children." I found the samples she chose to be consistent with her characterization. Shannon had given her class a set of arithmetic exercises, 35 one-digit addition problems and 35 one-digit subtractions. This struck me as a fairly typical math assignment for fourth graders early in the year when using a conventional math series. Shannon's report of her students' performance contained little mathematical content. Instead, she commented on their attitudes and behaviors:

Student A: very confident, neat and careful work

Student B: disinterested, shows minimal understanding

Student C: time on task minimal, very disorganized, needs fine motor skills

I saw no evidence from the task that Shannon's students were expected to explain how they arrived at their answers, and no indication from her analyses that the study of mathematics involved more than arithmetic computation. Since Shannon chose to share this assignment with the seminar, I assumed it was typical of work in her classroom. Taken together, her students' work and her analyses strongly suggested that Shannon viewed mathematics as a sequence of computational procedures that she needed to demonstrate and her students needed to practice and memorize.

Given her initial attitude, it surprised me when, two sessions into our seminar, Shannon became intrigued by the idea that mathematics problems can be solved in a variety of ways. In response to assignment 3, "What ideas about the number system have been highlighted for you?" she wrote that she had learned

> . . . there are many different ways to approach the solution to a given problem. However in my class the traditional +, –, carrying, and borrowing are always done first. Possibly this is done because we have no manipulatives to work with and therefore no other avenues are explored. I really don't even know if these manipulatives were ever offered to them in the lower grades, other than for the child who needed "hands on" extra help to solve the problem.

It interested me that although Shannon wrote that she now believed math problems could be done in a variety of ways, she still expected her students to use the traditional algorithms. I was also struck by her observation that, if her students had encountered manipulatives in earlier grades, it must have been as a tool for remediation. These comments suggested that Shannon was thinking not only about *what* her students had been taught in the past, but also about *how* they had been taught. I thought she might be questioning whether her students' approaches, which she had characterized elsewhere as "uncreative," were, after all, a result of their past school experience, rather than an expression of their inherent limitations.

Shannon continued to ask herself what her students would do with manipulatives, so she used the fourth assignment, "Conduct and write up a math interview," to explore this question.

> Never having used base ten blocks, I decided to borrow a sampling of them and just see exactly what my students would do with them. Would they even know what they were? I decided to work with Felicita, a student who has been mainstreamed this year from a bilingual class. She is struggling in all her subjects.

> I put the base ten blocks on the table and asked Felicita if she knew what these were and what they were used for. She said that she used them in the third grade and if you're [doing] math these are the ones, tens, and hundreds.

> I then asked her to show me a number like 124, and this is what she put together:

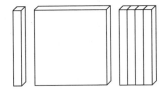

When I asked how many ones are there in 124 she said 1, and 4 tens, and 10 hundreds. Felicita sensed that this wasn't right and changed her base ten blocks to this arrangement:

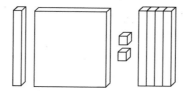

I then asked her what the large square represents, and she said hundreds; the long rod, she said tens; and the unit cube, she said ones. Felicita knew their value this way.

Then I wrote 124 on a paper next to the base ten blocks and asked her to show me the number now. She set up the blocks like this:

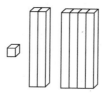

When pointing to 124, she did know that the 4 represented the ones; the 2, tens; and the 1, a hundred. "Yep!" she said "It's wrong. Oh! This is wrong, too."

She changed her blocks again so that 124 looked like this:

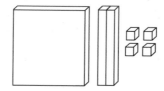

Now I gave her the number 356, and she put out these blocks:

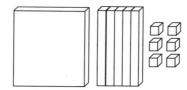

We went over how many ones, tens, and hundreds there are in 356. I said, "Everything matches except the hundreds."

Building a System of Tens

When asked how many hundreds are in 356, Felicita said 3. "How are you going to show me those 3?" I asked. She then made this arrangement:

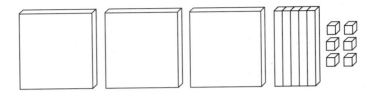

When I gave her 478, there was no hesitation. She used 4 of the hundreds, 7 of the tens, and 8 of the ones. Now I asked her to show me *any* number with ones, tens, and hundreds. She arranged this:

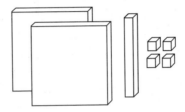

I wrote 224. She said, "Nope! Maybe this will help you!" And she rearranged the blocks so they looked like this:

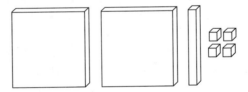

I still showed that I didn't quite understand. So, she changed all the blocks to the same color and said, "Perhaps this will help you."

I said, "214," and she felt success.

At this time I thought Felicita had regained her memory of the base ten rods and was going to end our little interaction. But then she put 10 tens together and said, "This is a hundred, too! So if you needed more hundreds, you can make them; and you can put ones together to make tens." I acted surprised, she was pleased, and we ended here.

Shannon used this assignment as an opportunity to see how the base ten blocks could be used to represent numbers. Given her lack of experience with these materials and her sense that they were useful only for remedial work, I saw Shannon's incorporation of the blocks into her interview as a courageous step. And I noted that she was exploring with one of her own students a mathematical issue—the relationships among hundreds, tens, and ones—that was foregrounded in the first few sets of cases in the *Building a System of Tens* casebook. Of particular interest to me was her recognition of the significance of Felicita's almost off-hand comment that 10 of the tens rods would make 1 hundred and 10 of the ones would make 1 ten.

I was also struck by Shannon's insistence that Felicita's arrangement of 214 blocks represented 224. Though Shannon doesn't reflect on this encounter, or tell us why she chose this approach, it seemed to me intended to get Felicita to be more explicit about her thinking. I wondered if Shannon considered adding this strategy to her routine practice. In her response to the fifth assignment, "Reflect on your reaction to the seminar so far," she herself touched on this point in a general way.

> What I question now is if this one way of teaching [the teacher explains and the students practice] is enough, or would using a combination of traditional and some new ideas I've gained since taking this course be better? Change is good for both me and my students, but too much change too fast is not the way to go either.

> After reading some of the situations given in our assignments, I ask myself how can I take this approach with my students if I don't even understand it. Help! I say. Yes, I need change, but how? When? Where? Why? And no traditional algorithm papers to send home to parents. How would they react? Whole language didn't go over well, now this! I need a shot of courage!

Shannon was expressing anxiety over the consequences of changing her teaching, even though she now seemed to feel that some changes would benefit her students. Much of this anxiety stemmed from a lack of confidence in her ability to sustain a different approach. Her concluding plea indicated both a desire to change and a need for support.

In my written response to Shannon, I encouraged her to continue thinking about connections between what she was experiencing in the seminar and her own classroom instruction. I reassured her that whether and how she changed was under her control: "This is important for you to realize—you are the one to decide and you are the one to implement whatever changes you want, at whatever pace you want."

In the next seminar meeting, Shannon wrote in reply:

> As I read your response to my writing, I realized that as much as I think change and new ideas are good, I am afraid to try it without complete knowledge. It's hard for me to learn as I go along, and it doesn't give me that safe and secure feeling. Your suggestion to take small steps is less threatening and should help me along. . . .
> "Flexible thinking" for both me and my students! We can learn together. Hopefully I'll be able to even understand their way of solving a problem (my greatest fear).

Shannon was moving from talking about change in a general way to identifying a specific concern: If she allowed her students the freedom to solve problems any way they wanted, perhaps she would not be able to understand their work. Is her worry grounded in her fear that she doesn't know enough mathematics?

In the assignment for Session 7, "Choose a case from the casebook or the video [for *Building a System of Tens*] and describe its impact on you," Shannon chose to write about the mathematical ideas she was encountering in the seminar; this indicated she was using the seminar as a means to think more deeply about mathematics for herself. Thus, she described a small-group discussion in which three different ways to solve $159 \div 13$ had been advanced. Her ideas about math began to shift when she was able to "see" repeated subtraction as a method of division. Shannon wrote about the incident this way:

> Our discussion/interaction about our division readings and the different ways to solve one problem was my enlightening point. In my group we did it [$159 \div 13$] the "regular way" [the division algorithm], then by equally distributing base ten rods, [and then] by just going around and counting out by ones. Then you came to our group and $159 \div 13$ suddenly became $159 - 13 = 146$, $146 - 13 = 133$, $133 - 13 = 120$, . . . and so on.
>
> I had never before thought of division as directly related to subtraction or, to go further, multiplication as part of addition. As simple as it sounds that one interaction really made an impact on me, as $\times$ and $\div$ were just something I did by a rote method, with not much thought as to how $+$, $-$, $\times$, and $\div$ are all related. I will be sure to incorporate these relationships in my multiplication and division lessons within my class.

I was excited to see that Shannon's ideas about mathematics were expanding. She was noticing the importance of understanding relationships among the operations and also acknowledging that thinking about mathematics this way was new to her. I was encouraged by her intention, expressed at the end of the excerpt, to make these new ideas part of her lessons on multiplication and division. This strong statement was in such sharp contrast to her earlier concern, and even trepidation, about changing her instruction. Although I was not sure in what way her teaching would reflect her new understandings, I was impressed with the strength of her resolve.

Some participants used the "pick-a-favorite-case" assignment to write about their changing view of mathematics, as had Shannon, but others had written about how the cases helped them rethink their teaching. In particular, several wrote about how they were listening to their students differently. I thought it might be useful for the entire group to have an overview of the ideas that had been raised in their papers. As I read through all the responses, three main themes emerged: listening for student thinking, perceiving the

Two Portraits of Change

authors of the cases as classroom teachers like themselves, and learning mathematics for oneself. I wrote a summary of participant comments, organized by those three categories, and distributed it at the next seminar session.

In some ways, Shannon's response to the last written assignment in the first seminar incorporates all three of these themes. The assignment was, "Write a case based on discussions in your own classroom." Having taken back to her class both a problem and a teaching strategy she had read about in the cases, Shannon described what happened when she asked her "traditionally taught" students to solve that problem in more than one way and to use manipulatives.

> For my case, I started with an idea from chapter 5, on multiplication. I chose the exact problem used out of *Investigations* which asks the children to solve 27×4 in two different ways.
>
> To give some background to my class, I would like to say that we have [another textbook] series, 1985 edition. There are no manipulatives with our book. However, I did get a manipulative kit in November, but the new edition books will be ordered for next year. My class is used to doing traditional algorithms the traditional way, with no use of base ten blocks.
>
> I wrote on the board, "Solve 27×4 in two different ways." We had just started with multiplication of multidigit numbers, so it was very timely. I let my math group work with partners for their strategies. After they had worked a while, I asked for volunteers to come to the board and show me some different ways to solve this problem. Steve started with this:
>
> $$\begin{array}{r} \overset{2}{27} \\ \times\ 4 \\ \hline 108 \end{array}$$
>
> He explained it: "$4 \times 7 = 28$, put down the 8 and carry the 2. $4 \times 2 = 8$, plus 2 = 10." Very traditional, but I would expect that, as this is the most common way they have been taught.
>
> Next was Kevin, showing a different way. He put down $4 \times 20 \times 7$ and said, "$4 \times 20 = 80$," but was stumped the rest of the way. I asked him for his work paper and saw this:
>
> $$4 \times 20 \times 7$$
>
> Then I asked him how he could write it differently. His answer was "$4 \times 20 = 80$ and $4 \times 7 = 28$. Then add, $80 + 28 = 108$."

Tanya had yet another way and proceeded to write down:

$$
\begin{array}{r}
2 \\
27 \\
27 \\
27 \\
+\ 27 \\
\hline
108
\end{array}
$$

She explained it as: "You are taking 27 four times, then adding them all up."

Elyshiana came next and wrote:

$$
\begin{array}{ccc}
54 & 50 + 50 = 100 & 100 \\
\times\ 2 & 4 + 4 = 8 & +\ 8 \\
\hline
108 & & 108
\end{array}
$$

She said there are other numbers that make 108, like 54 × 2. Then she took apart the 54 to make 50 + 4, two times, and then added up the answers.

My last student volunteer was Juan Carlos, who carefully and painstakingly put 27 fours on the board, recounted to make sure they were all there, and then added to the sum of 108.

I was very pleased with this episode and its results. My students did enjoy the challenge. However, when I asked which way they liked to solve the problem, they all said, "The regular way!" Traditional school/teacher = traditional class.

The next day, being so pleased with the ways to solve 27 × 4, I decided to ask them to use base ten blocks to show 27 × 4 two different ways. This was quite a bit harder and more frustrating for my math group. The following shows their efforts:

I feel that they are unfamiliar with, and really don't understand how to use, base ten rods as part of their math curriculum. This is an area we will have to gain strength in.

Shannon was now questioning her old assumptions. Early in the seminar, she had argued that her students would persist in solving problems the "traditional" way because of their past experiences in math classes. But this assignment showed Shannon was open to being surprised by her students. She had taken an example from one of the cases and investigated what would happen in her own classroom if she encouraged a more open-ended approach to the mathematics.

Reading the case Shannon wrote, I anticipated that her success with this problem would encourage her to continue experimenting with base ten blocks. Her attitude toward her students' inability to use the manipulatives had changed. Instead of passively accepting that her students' reactions were fixed—the result of traditional teaching—Shannon was now confident her students could "gain strength" in this area. I took this as an indication that she not only felt able to help her students increase their competence with the blocks, but also felt responsible for doing so.

I was reminded of our second session, when I had worried that some teachers in the seminar might be interpreting Janine's case as an advertisement for using manipulatives. How did Shannon think about them now? Had she adopted the simplistic view that manipulatives were "good," without thinking about what she wanted her students to learn by using them? Or did she see them as a tool that her students could use to express their mathematical ideas? I wasn't sure, but I was encouraged that she was willing to try some new approaches with her class, and I was curious to see if these changes would continue to develop as we worked through the next seminar.

Note: Shannon's portrait continues in the facilitator's guide for *Making Meaning for Operations.*

Claire: Working to change her teaching practice

While Shannon had entered the seminar with a traditional teaching practice, one that was quite similar to the way her own teachers taught when she was in elementary school, others arrived already oriented to a practice centered on their students' thinking and dedicated to the exploration of mathematical ideas. One of these, a first-grade teacher named Claire, enrolled in DMI after two years' experience working to change her practice. What would she contribute to the seminar and what would she take from it?

For the first assignment, collecting and analyzing three student work samples, Claire provided examples of her students' work on this word problem:

A farmer looking across his field sees two heads and six legs. He is such a long distance away he can't really tell who is behind the fence. Help the farmer think of possibilities. Who do you think might be behind the fence?

Claire had chosen a mathematical task that allowed her students to pursue a variety of solution strategies. In her analyses of their work, she paid attention both to the answers they gave and to the way their work matched their thinking process. In describing the student with whose work she was satisfied, Claire said that he "was able to offer more than one solution," that he "knew what was being asked for," and that he "kept precise track of the quantities involved." Of the two students about whom she was concerned, Claire indicated that one displayed "a lack of awareness when something didn't match what he was saying," that the other had "an inability to check her picture with what was being asked for," and that both had "weak self-monitoring skills." Among Claire's goals was a desire for her students to cultivate a variety of approaches to problem solving and to become aware of their own thinking processes.

Few others had brought in this kind of work. I wondered if the other participants in her small group had commented on her approach. Although I wanted her ideas to be part of the discussion, I didn't want to see Claire get set up as an expert. My concern was twofold—first, that the other participants would defer to her thinking without examining their own ideas; and second, that Claire wouldn't see that the seminar had something to offer her, too. I would have to keep an eye on this dynamic.

These concerns were soon lightened by evidence that Claire considered that her own experiences in the seminar could help her understand her students' learning. Despite Claire's head start over the other teachers, she seemed prepared to examine her own ideas. In her response to the third portfolio assignment, "What ideas about the number system have been highlighted for you?" Claire wrote:

At the conclusion of the math activity we did today, I found myself wondering how you keep asking yourself questions to keep your thinking and investigation moving forward. When I reached a dead end, it was difficult to keep formulating a question to direct my thinking. Sometimes I see connections readily and other times I don't. What can I do as a learner to help myself pose questions to lead to a connection? For me, this raises a question I have about my role as a teacher. Understanding our system of tens is challenging. How do I help my students ask themselves questions to challenge what they "think" they know so that they are able to make sense of their ideas? What helps a child hold onto multiple ideas and be able to use them flexibly and upon demand?

Claire expected her own learning experiences in the seminar to help her in her work as a teacher. Her attitude and the type of questions she was raising—for instance, how do students learn to ask themselves probing questions, and how do they develop the ability to hold onto multiple ideas—attested to her belief that her students were capable of complex mental processes and that, as their teacher, her job was to help them cultivate these powers.

Claire's disposition to reflect on her own learning and to consider how her seminar experiences should affect her teaching practice was consistent with the goals of the DMI seminar. Yet, Claire was sometimes uncomfortable in our seminar because her ideas about teaching seemed so different from those of the other teachers in the group. She expressed this discomfort in response to assignment 5, "Reflect on your reaction to the seminar so far."

> At times I feel reluctant sharing my thoughts and ideas during class. It is not due to the atmosphere fostered by staff, but rather to my own sensitivity. I sense that, for many, this course is exposing them to a way of teaching mathematics that is new for them. As a result, I find myself reflecting [on] rather than expressing my thoughts. Although I don't usually consider myself a writer, I think that keeping a journal during this course would have been a constructive outlet for me. I trust that as the course moves forward, I will feel freer being myself.

> . . . When I think about what I am learning in this course, there is one thing that stands alone. Key for me is the awareness that the more I take in about the teaching and learning of mathematics, the more I realize the magnitude of what there is to learn in this arena. Just as it is so important for me to wrestle with new ideas until they make sense to me, so it is necessary for me to integrate my head knowledge into my inner self. It is my desire to reach that place within where my new understandings will give life to my teaching. It comes down to that tangible level where one moves beyond being able to verbalize new ideas and reaches for what really matters in the classroom. I find myself at the place of intensifying my efforts to take my craft of teaching to a higher dimension.

Although Claire used this opportunity to express unease about her role in the seminar, she also identified an overall personal goal: to put into practice what she has come to understand intellectually. As I reflected on her comments, I realized that Claire and I had the same concern about her role as a member of the group. In my response to her writing, I let Claire know that I thought she was engaging the ideas of the seminar in a thoughtful manner and that I welcomed her contributions in class.

I was also eager to reassure her that the seminar could be a learning experience for her and to suggest that she consider the varied makeup of the group as an opportunity for that learning. "Instead of feeling reluctant to share your ideas, perhaps you can pose questions that will move those ideas further, both your own and those of others. I often learn by having to articulate what I believe to someone who believes differently. The need to express my own ideas clearly forces me to articulate them in a way that is not essential when they remain part of an internal reflection process. It feels to me that the heterogeneity of the seminar participants can be used to push all of us to clearer and deeper understandings of the learning process."

In response, Claire indicated that she had been feeling more comfortable speaking her thoughts during the last seminar session. She also acknowledged she was finding value in the seminar meetings. "Indeed, I am learning from the other teachers as well as from the class activities. This stimulation helps me reflect and deepen my own understanding."

Claire's reflective writing provided further evidence for these sentiments. For example, in choosing a case from the casebook or video and describing its impact, Claire commented on a case that helped her reexamine her ideas about teaching.

> As I challenge my beliefs about how children learn math, I often find myself rethinking what I once thought to be true. Sometimes I struggle with being able to reexamine my former teaching methods because I am searching for something new. I find myself wanting to bypass the old to embrace the new. Yet, I recognize that a fresh perspective on some of my earlier teaching strategies can be valuable as well. So just by the title alone—"Why Do We Need Rules?"—I was drawn quickly to this teacher narrative. It grabbed my attention because it is the type of question I ask myself.

> . . . From an outsider's perspective, it appeared that when the teacher gave the students the opportunity to put their thoughts into words, they weren't able to organize their thinking to communicate their ideas. However, one can see it as a critical point in their learning process. Having seen their attempts to write the rules and recognizing their partial understanding, the teacher now has the opportunity to help students develop persistence in their learning. It is a valuable "life lesson" to learn that errors and confusion are a natural part of learning. Although disequilibrium is an uncomfortable feeling, it is a necessary ingredient in developing understanding.

> Additionally, this narrative acted as a reminder to me that my understanding of how to teach mathematics is "in process," just as is my students' learning. And when I find my class struggling to make sense of something new, I need to remember that it is a natural part of the process. Furthermore, I need to help them see it as natural, too.

I was struck, in Claire's response, by the degree to which she took responsibility for her own learning. She used this assignment as an opportunity to work through ideas on several levels. To Claire, confusion and error are a natural part of the process of learning, and learning may be taking place even when students are struggling. And she applied this idea to her own teaching, reminding herself that *her* understanding of how to teach mathematics was also "in process"—as if to imply that she, too, should expect to make errors, be confused, and struggle.

In this response, I saw Claire fully engaged in challenging her own ideas. Although her earlier writings were also positive and reflective, I felt that her comments here marked an important shift in her approach to the seminar. Claire was now writing as much to *herself* as to me, using this assignment to figure out what *she* believed.

Shortly thereafter, Claire had to miss a seminar session. To make up for her absence, she handed in a paper in which she reflected on the set of cases discussed at that session. Claire analyzed the differences in the way she was reading cases now from the way she had at the beginning of the seminar.

> When we were given classroom cases to read last September, I struggled as I tried to look deeper into them. I could usually follow a student's thinking as described but found it difficult to get beyond its surface meaning. It was not clear to me what I was looking for, but I knew there was something more than what I was able to glean from a thoughtful reading.

> Upon reading this new set of cases, I realize that my ability to see beyond the printed word is emerging. In my mind's eye, I find myself focusing more on the layers of understanding that support the mathematics the students are involved in. I recognize that many 'simple' procedures actually require a facility with numbers that is more complex than I had realized previously. Additionally, when the teacher has looked deeper into the construct of a student's thinking, it stands out to me.

Claire's strategy of reading to uncover the "layers of understanding that support the mathematics" gave her new insight into the ideas the students in the cases were grappling with, as well as a standard against which to measure her own work. I was thinking that the mathematical ideas of the next seminar might allow Claire to extend her ability to see additional layers of mathematics underneath seemingly simple math problems. In particular, the first chapter of *Making Meaning for Operations* looks at very young children's methods of solving problems that adults will consider to be addition, subtraction, multiplication, and division—and solving them successfully without knowing traditional computation methods. Since Claire teaches first grade, I was eager to see her reaction to this set of cases.

Note: Claire's portrait, along with Shannon's, continues in the facilitator's guide for *Making Meaning for Operations.*